Steam Engine Principles and their application on a small scale

by

N. G. CALVERT

BEng, PhD, FIMechE

CALVERT TECHNICAL PRESS

Southampton, London and Newcastle

CALVERT TECHNICAL PRESS

58 The Parkway, Bassett, Southampton, SO16 3PN, England

First Published 1991

Reprinted 1991, 1993, 1996, 1999, 2005

ISBN 0 9513620 0 3 (Hardback)
ISBN 0 9513620 1 1 (Paperback)

Printed in England by
Hobbs the Printers Ltd, Totton, Hampshire SO40 3WX

CONTENTS

PREFACE

It does not seem long ago that the reciprocating steam engine was so common as not to excite interest. Even in 1950 the theory of the engine was prominent in technical education, but this was a bit out of date. The engines themselves had all but vanished. Scrapyards were reaping a rich harvest. It was rather late when young people realised what they had all but missed. Then the preservation movement began.

Steam has been popular with model engineers ever since steam began. It must be remembered that James Watt himself had his interest aroused by a model of a Newcomen engine. Small-scale steam railways have never lost their appeal, but the steam launch has almost gone. A very few survive on waters such as Windermere and the River Thames. Now the intrinsic excellence of steam power for quite small boats, canoes and dinghies upwards, is realised as never before, not so much for the full scale replicas of the opulent Edwardian launch, though this has its place in the range of interest, but for boats of 4 m (13 ft) to 6 m (20 ft) which can be trailed behind a motor car.

This book aims at a conceptual treatment of the principles which lay behind the steam plant which was so common in the nineteen-twenties and thirties. Information comes from day-to-day experience at the time, from the proceedings of the learned societies, both local and national, and from engineering journals.

This is no plea for a return to power produced by hand-fired coal. Stokeholds and the black industrial towns made too deep an impression for that, but on a small scale steam power does possess an appeal which no other prime mover has ever attained. One can mention the rural sawmill, agricultural engines, the branch railway meandering up a wooded valley, and most impressive of all, the steam launch almost ghostly in its silence as it sweeps round the islands. Furthermore it is a technology to which most people can attain if they are interested, and it is one which can often be locally self-sufficient.

The young people of today have no opportunity to enjoy the things which were possible fifty years ago. Who could now go to sea, in a working capacity, on an Atlantic liner driven by quadruple expansion engines? Or who, for a few shillings, could pound up the Welsh coast to the Menai Straits in a 20 knot paddle steamer? It is for them, steam enthusiasts from many walks of life, and for engineers who now work in less glamorous fields, that this book has been written.

Those who are introduced by this book to the elements of steam plant will find a number of terms peculiar to this subject explained in the glossary.

May 1983

Editor's Note

Geoffrey Calvert wrote this book as a companion to his *Wind Power Principles: their application on a small scale* (ISBN 0 85264 258 X, Charles Griffin, 1979); he was not, however, able to arrange for its publication before his death in 1984. It is published now by his family and friends in memory of a true steam engineer and enthusiast.

We gratefully acknowledge Edward Paget-Tomlinson, Eileen Harrison and Monica Boothroyd who drew the illustrations which appear at the beginning of each chapter.

LIST OF FIGURES

CHAPTER 1

How it Began

Narrow Gauge Railway

An impression of the Ravenglass and Eskdale Railway, Cumbria. Built as a mineral line, it was later revised on a narrower gauge. Although it is mainly a tourist line it nevertheless published (in 1982) a year-round time-table.

We believe that the first man to drive a piston with steam pressure was Newcomen, an ironmonger from Dartmouth. This was in the early eighteenth century. His engine was used for draining mines, and it depended entirely on the force produced by atmospheric pressure on one side of the piston. The cylinder on the other side of the piston was filled first with steam to the exclusion of air. A water jet was then turned into the steam, which being condensed produced a partial vacuum. His boiler was similar to a brewer's copper of the time and it worked at atmospheric pressure, or very slightly above it.

Watt's contribution was to separate the working cylinder and the condenser, thus saving heat. He also used low-pressure steam instead of air above the piston, thus still further saving heat. Watt obtained long-lasting patents on the use of a separate condenser. This had a profound effect on development. Steam users had either to accept Watt's ideas and pay his dues, or avoid the use of a condenser. The alternative was the use of high pressures with atmospheric exhaust at a time when neither materials nor technology were up to it.

There were thus two separate lines of development. One was the low-pressure, low-speed condensing engine, a line initially followed both for stationary and marine engines. The other was a route which owes nothing to Watt; the use of high pressures and atmospheric exhaust. This of course led to the locomotive engine, a development which was to have the greatest influence on the reciprocating engines which we know today. When Watt's patents expired, condensers could be applied to high-pressure engines with a gain in economy and a saving of water, but the tendency to low speeds and large size persisted for a long time. Beam engines were apparently considered normal for factory work for another fifty years, and for waterworks pumping almost to the end of the 19th century.

The principal application of early steam power was to the draining of mines, and for this purpose the beam engine was developed. The steam cylinder stood on solid ground and operated one end of a pivoted beam. The other end of the beam worked over the pit shaft and the pump rods were suspended from it. Normally, the engine would be single acting, the weight of the pump rods providing power for the return stroke. Drop valves were used to control the steam flow. When the engine was adapted to produce rotary motion the beam form, or one of its derivatives, was often retained. One reason for this was that the piston rod could be guided along a sufficiently straight path by use of a linkwork. This could be readily produced on a forge and it had less friction than the cross-head slides of the day. These really had to await the advent of the planing machine. Thus arose a belief that even when the beam was dispensed with, the proper place for the cylinder was on the ground with the crank shaft and motion above it. The ponderous scantlings of the early engines might not have worked so well in a horizontal position. Thus the vertical engines of historical account had the crank above the cylinder. What we now consider to be a vertical engine was called an inverted engine.

Factory engines until well into this century were not self-contained on a single bed, but were often integral with the building. The various components, cylinders, bearings, etc., were loosely supported on masonry plinths, lined up with steel wedges and then grouted down. It was the locomotive which demanded a radically different approach. Features which we now regard as normal in a steam engine, the slide valve, double action and in many cases self starting, stem from this origin.

Varied duties performed by reciprocating steam engines

Much of this must now be read in the past tense.

Steam engines have been built to meet widely varying demands of duty, each requiring very special properties, yet to external inspection they may seem very much alike. The principal differences are in the setting of the valve, its lap, its lead and its angle of advance, and in the number of cranks and their relative positions. A few examples are listed below.

- Locomotive engines must start from any position. Whilst they must be able to exert their maximum torque at zero speed, they must yet be capable of economic running at relatively low loads and high speeds, as when a train is on a gentle down grade.
- An engine required to drive an electrical generator must run at constant speed and show its greatest economy near to its maximum load. Self-starting is not important; such engines can be barred round to a favourable starting position if need be.
- A marine engine must always be self-starting and have a high degree of manoeuvrability in either direction. It must show its best economy at a fairly high load.
- Crane engines have to exert a big initial haul. They must be able to hold their load suspended in mid-air and then lower it gently where it is required. A pit winding engine must be capable of great power and controlled acceleration, and be sensitive enough to stop the cage exactly where required.
- A ship's anchor winch must exert a strong live pull as the anchor is retrieved from the mud, even though it is mounted on the stem of a pitching ship. The engine must exert this steady pull even if momentarily stalled, or even forced into reverse direction.
- Ships' steering engines have the property of a servo-motor. They must copy exactly what the quartermaster does with the steering wheel on the bridge, move a fraction when the steering wheel moves a fraction, accelerate, or stop, or reverse almost instantly as is required.
- Perhaps the greatest impression of utterly relentless force is the engine which drives the cogging rolls in a steel works. These take the first bite at a white-hot ingot of steel, reducing it in section and increasing its length, a process which may continue in subsequent rolls until literally miles of wire or thin sheet emerge from the further end.

Rational applications for today

The efficiency of small steam plant is low, which means that a lot of the heat released in the furnace is rejected in the exhaust: perhaps more than 95% of it. Hence a rational application is to use steam plant when the rejected low grade heat can be usefully used along with the required power. The heating of buildings such as hotels or hospitals comes to mind; this is done to some extent.

Some industrial processes, particularly sawmills, leave a lot of waste behind them, which if burned in a boiler can produce enough power for the mill. This was formerly quite often done, but the cheapening of electricity along with the increase in firemen's labour costs has often led to its abandonment, sometimes with an embarrassing accumulation of the waste produced. These relative costs could change.

From a recreational point of view, the author considers inland pleasure boating to be one ideal application of steam. The plant is quiet and unobtrusive. Many, many times has the author spent a day afloat on canal, river or lake, for no more cost than the gathering of a few sticks from the forest floor, or the burning of rotten woodwork discarded in house repair, perhaps supplemented by the gathering of driftwood as he steamed along.

Narrow gauge railways were at one time considered the solution to rural transport problems. One hundred years ago systematic experiments were made to determine the smallest practical size for a working (as opposed to a miniature) railway. The conclusion was a gauge of 15 inches. Narrow gauge railways were built for the great estates and others for the extraction of minerals. In one case a railway only became viable when the gauge was reduced. New narrow gauge lines have recently been laid on the trackways of abandoned main lines. Small railways are mainly of tourist and enthusiast significance, yet even now some operate the whole year round. No one can safely say that these little railways may not yet have a part to play.

CHAPTER 2

On Matters Fundamental

R.M.S. Segwun

The last of the Muskoka Lakes (Ontario, Canada) steamships, her name means 'Springtime'. These ships maintained the mail service from 'ice out' in May to 'freeze up' in December. In 1958 they were superseded. Segwun has recently been restored by voluntary effort.

The states of matter

The solid, liquid and gaseous states are well known. To Sir Oliver Lodge are attributed the statements:

- A solid has fixed shape and volume;
- A liquid has fixed volume but not shape;
- A gas has neither fixed shape nor volume.

This is of course a simplification. Between the liquid and the gas is the vapour state of which steam is a very common example.

Many engineering problems are explained by the pre-nuclear concept of the atom: that of an ultimate and indivisible particle. Such particles can aggregate together, united by elastic bonds to form molecules. It is the motion of the molecules which leads to the concept of temperature. As the motion increases (vibration motion in a solid, mostly free-flight motion in a gas) what we know as 'hotness' increases. As the motion slows down, hotness decreases. There must be a limit to slowing down, so there is a lower limit to coldness. This is known as the absolute zero of temperature. Nothing colder can exist. If the Celsius (Centigrade) degree interval is used, absolute zero (unattainable by man) is at 273 degrees below the freezing point of water (460 degrees below zero on the Fahrenheit scale). Temperatures measured from absolute zero (using the °C interval) are called degrees K (Kelvin). Thus the comfortable temperature of 10°C (50°F) can also be written as 283°K.

Kinetic theory

Pressure as well as temperature in a gas or vapour can also be explained in terms of the simple molecular model. As molecules in free flight strike and bounce off the containing vessel, they exert a force on it (just as myriads of tennis balls constantly being driven against and bouncing off a wall would together exert a force on the wall). The force on a unit area of the wall (square metre or square inch) is the pressure. In this respect in a gas the molecules are in free and independent flight. In a vapour such as steam groups of molecules are bunched together, not having acquired sufficient energy to tear themselves completely apart. In a solid they are in a state of vibration which is not violent enough to separate them.

Specification of pressure

Pressure as well as temperature in everyday life is measured from an arbitrary datum - that is the pressure of the atmosphere. This is because it is easier to make a gauge which reads upward from the atmosphere's pressure than it is to make one which reads from an absolute zero. A barometer, however, is an example of an absolute pressure gauge.

Referring now to figure 2.1, the pressure at the point A can be specified either as

(1)   gauge pressure above atmosphere, or

(2)   absolute pressure above zero.

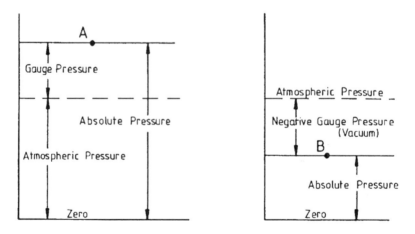

Figure 2.1
Specification of pressure

At the point B the pressure is below that of the atmosphere. The pressure measured below the atmosphere is commonly referred to as the vacuum at B. This is rather loose terminology, but is widely used.

The way in which the liquid and vapour states of matter merge into each other can be illustrated by a chart in which the pressure of a fixed mass of substance is related to its volume. On this are drawn lines of constant temperature (figure 2.2).

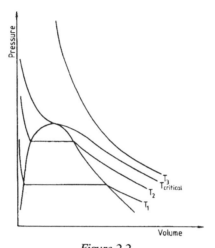

Figure 2.2

Pressure–volume isothermals

Two properties have now been introduced: pressure and temperature. Two more are necessary, and the specification of the mass considered is required. This is generally taken as unity. Thus the specific volume of a fluid may be written as m^3/kg or ft^3/lb. The inverse of the specific volume is the density. A fourth property is called the entropy. This has no physical existence and it has an arbitrary datum, but its changes can be precisely calculated. Such changes are listed in tables and plotted on charts. It is unprofitable to try to find an analogue for entropy. There is none. It must be accepted and used. It is as much of a handicap to try to understand what is going on in your steam engine without recourse to entropy tables or charts as it is for a coastwise navigator to reject the tide tables. In both cases the tables are prepared by the learned and they are intended to be used without question by the practical man. Entropy is generally denoted by the letter S. Even so, the only use of entropy in this book is a conceptual treatment in Chapter 15.

There are four fundamentals – pressure, temperature, specific volume and entropy. In general any two define the state of a substance, but there is an exception when three are required. This exception is in the region where the simple steam engine must operate. The engine always has to work in that peripheral region where exact data cannot exist. That is why engineering is allied to the creative arts.

Energy, work and heat

Energy is one of the fundamentals of the universe, which can appear in many forms. Heat and work are transient manifestations of energy which sometimes appear when it is changing from one form to another. Energy arrives in a radiant form from the sun. We can sense its presence when it adopts the transient form of heat. Energy may be stored in a chemical form by organic nature. We cannot sense the energy in a lump of coal until it begins to burn, when again we sense the transient presence of heat. The energy in a mountain lake is in a potential form. If, under controlled conditions, the water is led down a pipe it can be made to form a jet. The transient form of work can then be exhibited on a turbine wheel.

Energy is not destroyed: it can only undergo change. A form which can produce the transient of work is a high-grade energy. One which cannot is a low-grade form. Energy always tends to go spontaneously to a lower grade. The reverse process, the spontaneous upgrading of energy, does not take place. In the old classical terms, the energy of the universe is constant, but the entropy always tends to increase.

The working substance

Energy requires a physical medium if mechanical work is to be produced. Water-steam and combustion gases are well known examples but they are not the only ones. Solid materials are used in special cases, such as in some forms of thermostat.

Work can only be obtained if there is an orderly change of state. The energy of steam in a boiler is made up of the random motion of aggregations of molecules. If the pressure is reduced in an orderly way behind a retreating piston, the transient of work can appear on the piston (and thus at the engine shaft). As some of the molecules bounce off the piston, they leave some of their energy with it and retreat more slowly. Mention may again be made of the fact that to extract all the energy of the molecules they would have to be expanded until they were brought to rest, or until they had cooled down to absolute zero of temperature. This is impossible in an engine system having a net delivery of work. They can only be cooled to the lowest surrounding temperature, that is the temperature of the surrounding medium, such as the atmosphere or the sea.

Reversibility of energy

A fundamental and illuminating idea is that of reversibility. If a process in which energy forms are changed can be reversed, then both forms of energy are of the same grade. This implies that there has been no degradation, or that the process was a perfect one. The degree of reversibility then is a criterion of perfection. Rapid compression of a gas by a piston can often be followed by rapid expansion as the piston bounces back, thus restoring some of the compression work. This process is nearly reversible. Electrical accumulators and power storage reservoirs are cases of partial reversibility which are put to practical use. Friction dissipating work into heat is wholly irreversible. Bringing a vehicle to rest by means of friction brakes leaves the braking surfaces hot. It is impossible to imagine the reverse process of the cooling of the brakes setting the vehicle into motion again.

The cyclical process

Power production always involves a discontinuous process, even though superficially it sometimes appears to be continuous.

This principle was well brought out in the last century when for instructional purposes Professor Ewing envisaged a hypothetical engine consisting of a long metal rod. This was fixed at one end and at the other connected to a ratchet and pawl device mounted on a rotatable shaft. When the rod was heated the wheel could be rotated by one ratchet notch as the rod expanded. When the rod was cooled, it would shorten so as to get the pawl back into position for the next thrust. This emphasises the cyclical nature of the engine process. The essential features are (1) a working substance, in this case the rod, (2) a hot source, say a Bunsen burner flame under the rod, (3) a heat sink, say a wet rag wrapped round the rod. The amount of work done would depend on the difference between the maximum and minimum temperatures attained by the rod. An isolated device such as a jet engine in which cold air and fuel flow in and hot gas flows out, taken in isolation, appears continuous, but when a wider view is taken it can be seen that somewhere the hot discharge gases must cool down and ultimately reach the inlet conditions.

Negative work

The acceptance of the cyclical process implies that the working substance must get back to its original state so as to be in a position to start again. This means that both positive and negative work occur in any heat engine system. Positive work is associated with the giving of heat and an increase in volume; negative work with the rejection of heat and the diminishing of volume. In a steam plant the negative mechanical work (that is, the energy absorbed by the boiler feed pump) is quite small. This limitation of negative work, more than any other factor, made the steam engine the first practical thermo-power plant. In a gas turbine the negative work is large. This delayed its practical appearance until the resources of an advanced industrial society were available. Indeed, on some of the early gas turbine sets little, if any, net power was available, all the output of the turbine being required to drive the compressor.

The basic principles

The science of thermodynamics lies behind the study of engines (and much else besides). It is interesting to know in retrospect that the age dominated by the reciprocating steam engine had passed its peak before the laws of thermodynamics were fully appreciated, yet now we know that on a macro scale they are the most fundamental principles known to man. They are probably impossible to prove, but any assumption that they are not true leads to conclusions which are clearly at variance with universal experience. One of the difficulties with the second law in particular is in its formulation. What to one person may appear to be a statement of the law may seem to another to be a deduction from an alternative statement. The apparent vagueness can lend itself to ridicule from the vulgar. When the (rather unreal) controversy of the two cultures was at its height, a counter attack by the scientific school was that to be innumerate was as much a thing to be ashamed of as to be illiterate, and that an understanding of the second law of thermodynamics was the hallmark of an educated person.

The laws of thermodynamics

There are four laws of thermodynamics of which the first and second most concern the engineer. Subsequent to their acceptance philosophers found that they required a preliminary statement before the first law could be discussed. This statement, the last to be formulated, was called the Zeroth Law, so as not to disturb the familiar numbering of the first and second.

The first law recognises that heat and work are transient forms of energy. It disposed, once and for all, of the earlier theories of a caloric substance.

Implicit in the second law is the idea of an absolute scale of temperature, and the excellence of a reversible process. It states that energy cannot spontaneously pass from a lower to a higher grade, and that, if work is to be done in a heat engine process, then the temperature of the energy source (i.e. the boiler) must be higher than that of the energy sink (e.g. the condenser).

The first and second laws together refute the possibility of perpetual motion in any form.

The third law, of concern to physicists, states that the absolute zero of temperature is unattainable.

A facetious, but nevertheless sound, interpretation is:

First law – you cannot win, but might break even,
Second law – you can only break even at absolute zero,
Third law – absolute zero is unattainable.

Maxwell's demon

This is an approach to the second law of thermodynamics from the molecular point of view.

A mass of gas separated into two parts by a partition is postulated. In the partition is a door which can be opened and closed by a demon who can recognise individual molecules and assess their speeds. When a fast molecule is approaching, the demon opens the door and lets it through. When a slow one approaches, the door is kept closed and the molecule bounces off. Similarly, slow molecules are allowed to escape from the other side, and fast ones are not allowed through. Thus in the course of time, the gas on one side of the partition gets hotter and that on the other side gets cooler. Apparently the second law is confounded. We conclude that Maxwell's demon cannot exist.

Efficiency

In common usage the concept of efficiency is often confused with that of reliability or of effectiveness. In engineering it has only one meaning. It is the ratio of useful energy output to the energy input in a machine or process.

In a steam engine process, the ultimate test is between the thermal energy in the fuel and the mechanical energy available on the output shaft. An efficiency so defined could be called the shaft thermal efficiency, or since shaft power is often measured on a dynamometer brake, the brake thermal efficiency.

Component efficiencies can be defined, dealing with the boiler, the steam cycle of events in the engine, and the mechanical properties of the engine itself. The brake thermal efficiency would then be the product of all the component efficiencies.

Such examination of each step in a process may be enlightening in showing where there is most scope for improvement.

The Carnot cycle

The processes by which a substance can change in state, which are often of use, are those which take place at constant temperature and those which take place without heat flowing into or out of the substance. These are called isothermal and adiabatic changes, respectively. An extra restriction placed on the adiabatic change is that it may also be free from internal friction. The ideal process can be called an adiabatic and frictionless change. Or it can be called an isentropic change.

It can be deduced from the second law of thermodynamics that no cycle can be more efficient than one in which all the heat is given at the highest temperature of the cycle and all the heat rejected at the lowest temperature of the cycle.

Such a cycle is called the Carnot cycle. There must then be four stages. Two are called isothermals in which the heat is given (or rejected) at constant temperature, and two are called isentropics in which heat is neither given nor rejected.

In the steam cycle the isothermal giving of heat is obvious in the evaporation process and its rejection in that of condensation. The expansion of the steam through the engine can aim at being adiabatic and isentropic but the feed pump and feed heating process do not approach this ideal.

It is generally considered that the Carnot ideal is not realistic from a steam plant point of view. A less demanding basis for comparison, called the Rankine cycle, is more realistic.

CHAPTER 3

Water-Steam

Douglas Head Steam Ferries

These operated from the base of the Victoria Pier to the Battery Pier in Douglas harbour, Isle of Man. The vessels were rectangular in deck plan and had four propellers, two at each side, being coupled through. This service was abandoned in about 1939.

The water-steam substance is uniquely suitable as a working substance for a terrestrial heat engine power plant. Its properties are such that it can be adapted to small sizes of engine with simple, even primitive engineering or to the largest sizes of power plant which man has been able to contemplate. Some of its desirable properties are listed below.

(1)   widely available in the natural world;

(2)   non-poisonous;

(3)   not significantly corrosive to most engineering materials;

(4)   a pressure-volume relationship which is convenient relative to normal atmospheric temperature;

(5)   a large change in volume between steam and water which means that an engine can be devised which has very small negative work.

Dry and saturated steam

A strong metal vessel fitted with a pressure gauge, a thermometer and a safety valve can be used to illustrate some of the properties of water-steam.

The vessel is partially filled with water and has all the air above the water expelled by steam after heating. It is then closed and allowed to settle down to a steady state. A certain pressure and temperature can then be observed. The pressure is said to be that corresponding to the temperature, and the steam in the space above the water is said to be *dry and saturated*: dry because our postulated steady state means that any particles projected out of the water into the space above are balanced by steam particles diving back again; saturated because the space when in contact with the water can only contain a fixed amount of vapour. The introduction of more vapour would lead to the excess being condensed into the water. The removal of vapour would lead to more evaporation until equilibrium was restored. So deep rooted in ordinary usage is the association of saturation with wetness that the term *dry and saturated* may at first appear to be a contradiction.

If further heat is applied, then another set of corresponding pressure and temperature can be observed. With sufficient readings a unique curve (figure 3.1) of corresponding pressure and temperature can be plotted.

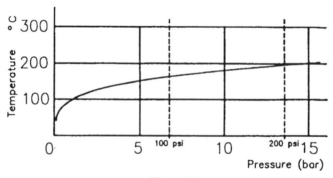

Figure 3.1

Corresponding Pressure and Temperature

Saturated steam in contact with water cannot be made hotter without increasing its pressure. However if it is removed from the water from which it is formed its temperature can be raised as far as practical circumstances permit. Such water vapour which is at a higher temperature than that which corresponds to its pressure is called superheated steam. The higher the temperature above that of saturation the more do the properties approach those of a gas.

In practice dry and saturated (D & S) steam is rare. The formation of steam bubbles within the water and their projection into the space above inevitably puts particles of water into suspension in the steam. These are entrained and carried away with the steam supply. To some extent water can be removed from steam by mechanical separation, but complete removal generally needs the application of heat after the steam has left the boiler.

The formation of steam, so described, is a constant volume process. This process is used as a demonstration in technical teaching and it is approximated to in the domestic pressure cooker. However, for power purposes steam is raised not at constant volume but at constant pressure, during what is described as a flow process. Water and energy flow into the boiler and steam flows out.

The rigorous treatment of any thermodynamic process needs mathematical preparation at a level to which few people attain. However this does not prevent others from the enjoyment of acquiring a mental picture of the process which is adequate for much practical work.

Steam tables

For approximately one hundred years engineers have had recourse to tables of the properties of steam. These are calculated from mathematical models of the way in which water-steam behaves. Constants needed for the computation come from experiment. Over the years mathematical models become more refined and experiments more precise. From time to time new tables are published. Differences are mainly in the high pressure and temperature region. Tables published in the present century have hardly altered by much more than one per cent in the low pressure saturated region – that is 0 to 15 bars (210 lb/in^2).

Until fairly recently tables referred to *heat of formation*, that is *sensible heat*, *latent heat* and *superheat* for the successive stages in the change from water to superheated steam. This terminology is now considered unsatisfactory from a philosophical point of view. An alternative term *enthalpy* has been invented. This is now used in most steam tables. It is often denoted by the letter h, with a suffix indicating the state referred to. The author has decided to present both terminologies for this conceptual treatment of the subject. An engineer might readily understand either terminology but a non-specialist might have a little extra difficulty in understanding the new one.

A full set of steam tables is an impressive document. Properties are tabulated at close intervals and given to many significant figures. Further, the column headings need fairly advanced knowledge for their understanding. Fortunately, they are rarely needed except by designers of advanced steam plant.

For more general purposes, such as technical education, more modest abridged tables are available. These can readily be obtained from a university book shop. The data can also be presented on a large chart where lines of constant pressure, enthalpy and other properties are plotted on axes of temperature and entropy. Figure 3.4 is a greatly simplified diagram of this type.

For the general reader to whom this book is addressed the graphical representations of figures 3.2 and 3.4 should suffice. Indeed, the old mechanic's rule that it took 1000 B.Th.U. to form one pound of steam from available feed water is unlikely to be more than 10% in error over moderate pressure ranges.

Three stages are envisaged in the formation of unit mass (kg or lb) of steam:

(1)   *Sensible heat or hf*

The first stage is to raise the temperature of the water from that of the supply to that corresponding to the evaporation pressure. If this were carried out in a separate feed heater a temperature difference between inlet and outlet could be observed by means of thermometers. For this reason the old engineers referred to sensible heat, meaning the heat obviously going into the raising of water temperature.

(2)   *Latent heat or hfg*

Heat supplied for evaporation makes no difference to the temperature. The temperature of the steam leaving the boiler is the same as that of the water from which it has been formed. Thus heat manifestly entering but giving no indication on a thermometer is said to be latent. Alternatively, the latent heat of steam is that required to change the state of unit mass of water to dry and saturated steam at the same temperature.
The latent heat of steam is not a constant but falls as the temperature rises, becoming zero at the critical point.

(3)   *Superheat*

If steam is taken away from the water from which it was formed it can be raised to a temperature higher than that corresponding to the pressure. Such steam is said to be superheated. The higher the degree of superheat, the more its properties approach those of a gas. (A degree of ambiguity can arise since sometimes the term superheat is used to denote the temperature above saturation temperature and sometimes it refers to the extra energy which unit mass of the steam receives in the superheater.)

The properties sensible heat, latent heat and their sum — the heat of formation — are shown graphically in figure 3.2.

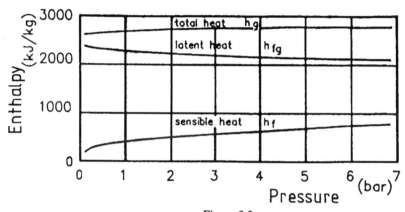

Figure 3.2
Sensible heat and latent heat

It can be seen that within the range plotted

(a)   the sensible heat h_f rises steadily,

(b)   the latent heat h_{fg} falls and would become zero at the critical point.

The sum of these, the heat of formation h_g rises quite slowly, about 4% between atmospheric pressure and 14 bar (210 lb/in^2). This small increase of heat of formation as the temperature rises may not seem consistent to people waiting for the pressure in a boiler to rise, but it can be explained. As the pressure rises, so does the temperature and there is a smaller temperature difference between the fire and the boiler surface.

Wet steam – dryness fraction

In practical terms the substance leaving the boiler is always a mixture of steam and water droplets. This is referred to as wet steam. The term *dryness fraction* means the amount of dry steam per unit mass of substance leaving the boiler. The lesser used term *wetness fraction* is unity minus the dryness fraction.

Expansion

Two extreme cases must be recognised. The first, which may be called resisted expansion, is that which is aimed at behind a piston on which work is being done. The expansion is meant to be orderly, not causing eddies or turbulence in the steam. As each molecule of steam bounces off the retreating piston it has given up some of its energy and thus comes away with a lower velocity. A corresponding expansion is aimed at in a turbine nozzle. The walls of the nozzle are cunningly shaped so that as much as possible of the random velocity of the molecule is turned into a unidirectional velocity of the stream leaving the nozzle. In the above cases, if the steam is still dry and if the process is an efficient one, the steam must get wetter as the expansion proceeds and energy passes either into the piston, or into the stream in the case of a turbine (*AB* in figure 3.3).

The second case, unresisted expansion, takes place when steam has its pressure dropped by a throttle valve. Here the object is to increase the disorder of the flow. The energy previously manifested by the pressure must appear as disordered velocity of the molecules in the form manifested by temperature. The steam now gets drier, or even superheated in an extreme case, since the temperature is lower than it was at the start but might be higher than that corresponding to the new pressure.

The throttle and the nozzle

Since it is a point which often causes confusion, the difference between a throttle and a nozzle should be emphasised.

A nozzle aims to guide the expanding fluid, as previously explained, so that random velocities of the molecules are turned into a uni-directional jet, characteristically to operate on a turbine wheel. This is done by the carefully calculated cross-section of the nozzle.

A throttle aims at dropping the pressure by expanding the fluid, but with a disordered flow so that any tendency to uniformity is dissipated into the random motion of the molecules. A reducing valve throttles the steam down to some pre-determined pressure and, as previously explained, it normally dries or even slightly superheats initially wet steam (*AD* on figure 3.3).

It was formerly marine practice to operate the main engines on wet steam (as delivered by the boiler) to provide for cylinder lubrication, but to bypass some of the steam into a reducing valve for use on auxiliary drives (say 215 lb/in^2 down to 160 lb/in^2).

The vertical line such as *AC* on figure 3.3 represents a change in which there was no heat flow in or out of the fluid and in which there was no internal friction. Consequently it may be called an adiabatic and frictionless change. Alternatively it is sometimes referred to as an isentropic change.

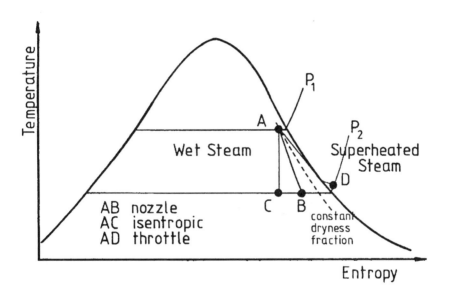

Figure 3.3
Steam Processes

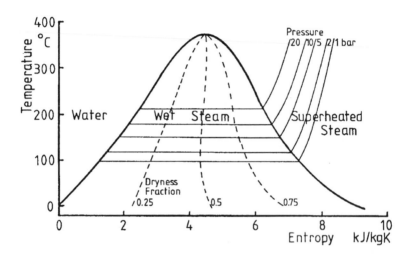

Figure 3.4
Properties of Steam

CHAPTER 4

The Combustion of Fuel and the Transfer of Heat

Garden Railways

Quarter scale models of welsh quarry locomotives on a 7½in gauge are eminently suitable for use on garden railways. This sketch is of a recent engine built by Barrowfold Engineering, Staveley-in-Cartmel.

Fuels are basically composed of carbon and hydrogen. In combustion the oxygen in the air combines with the carbon to form carbon dioxide, and with the hydrogen to form water vapour. Fuel quality carbon is similar to coke or charcoal but, fortunately for reasons of safety, hydrogen is not likely to appear by itself. Almost always it is combined with carbon. There are a very large number of hydrocarbon combinations, some appearing as gas or as light oils. These burn very readily. Others appear as heavy oils or as solids. These need to be heated and broken up before they can burn readily in air. The hydrocarbons in a solid fuel such as coal may be distilled off as smoke; this needs high temperature, gaseous turbulence and adequate time for complete combustion. The firebox should be large so that the flame reactions are not influenced by the nearness of water-cooled metal surfaces.

With the atmospheric oxygen there is an unavoidable introduction of nitrogen and very small amounts of other gases. These take no part in the combustion process, but nevertheless have to be heated up by the fire. Thus they dilute and lower the temperature of the combustion gases.

Excess air

In addition it is generally necessary to introduce an excess of air to make sure that all the fuel is burnt, and it is better to dilute the products further than to risk unburned fuel. The amount of excess air depends on the way the fuel is presented to the air. It can be quite small for a gaseous fuel, but more is needed with oil and much more with a solid fuel such as wood or coal.

On large plants, instruments display the percentage of carbon dioxide and unburned gases in the chimney stack. Thus adjustments can be made to keep combustion going under optimum conditions. On small plants much depends on the skill of the fireman.

Heat flow

Three mechanisms are involved in heat flow processes. They are known as conduction, convection and radiation respectively. In the condenser process conduction and convection predominate.

The three concepts are common enough to the human senses. The feeling of hotness or coldness when a metal surface is touched indicates conduction. The discomfort from a cold wind, which can be readily neutralized after a cloud passes from the face of the sun, gives a lively indication of convection followed by radiation.

Conduction

This is apparently the most simple of the principal modes of heat transfer. If a metal rod (preferably of copper for demonstration purposes) has one end exposed to a flame, in due course a rise in temperature can be observed at the other end. This is sometimes exploited in building small model boilers: copper rods can be brazed through the shell. The lower part exposed to the fire receives heat which is conducted up to the water surface on the other side of the shell. Conduction is a relatively slow process depending on vibration of the molecules exciting nearby ones until at the far end they excite the water which surrounds them.

Convection

By this mechanism hot fluid molecules approach the metal surface, but their effectiveness is hindered by the almost universal formation of a film when a fluid flows over a solid surface. Heat transfer through the film to the metal is in the nature of conduction and is correspondingly slow. Exactly the same thing happens when the heat flow tries to leave the metal to the fluid beyond. (Film resistance is diminished if the flow is turbulent, when it is in effect tending to scour the film away. A dramatic effect attributed to film concerns pinking, or detonative combustion, in an internal combustion engine. The shock waves from this type of combustion are believed so much to reduce the layer of gas on the piston top as to expose it to an increased heat flow, in some cases sufficiently severe as to melt the aluminium alloy.)

The film resistance to heat flow can be bigger than the resistance of the metal tube walls on which it is formed. This can lead to anomalous results in the comparison of tube materials. For an adequate convective heat flow to take place the flow should be turbulent, otherwise a very large area is needed.

Radiation

This is the name given to the transmission of energy through space, until it meets an absorbing surface where it can be manifested by a rise in temperature. The fact that few (if any) fully understand the mechanism does not prevent the phenomenon being put to good use. A special and familiar case is sunlight. Some objects are transparent to it, some reflect it, and others absorb it. Radiation travels in straight lines and the energy flux depends on the fourth power of the absolute temperature of the source.

A boiler engineer then, can benefit from an intense fire which can 'see' the bulk of the heat-absorbing surface.

For a long time the area of heating surface of a boiler has been considered to be a measure of its output. This is at best less than a half truth. Surfaces exposed to a radiant fire are much more effective than those exposed to hot gases alone. Eighty years ago eminent professors of engineering considered that concentrating attention on area was delaying boiler development. Even at that time experiments had shown that a locomotive firebox having only one tenth of the heating surface was responsible for half the evaporation.

Corresponding anomalies arose in the area of convected heat flow before the doctrine of the surface film or boundary layer was appreciated. Some experiments on fire-tube boilers had shown an improvement in performance when a number of tubes were plugged. This can now be readily explained. The higher velocities in the remaining tubes rendered the flow more turbulent and hence partially scoured away the film which was restricting heat flow. Again, experiments intended to compare the relative effectiveness of iron and copper tubes could be inconclusive. The reason for this was that the better conductivity of copper could be quite masked by small differences in the flow conditions.

Twisted sheets of metal were often placed in fire tubes. This imparted a swirling and more turbulent flow. Although they were sometimes called *retarders* in the stokehold, their intention was exactly the opposite. *Turbulence stimulators* might have been a better name.

CHAPTER 5

Steam is formed - Boilers

Mersey Ferries

These ferries worked between Liverpool and Birkenhead until replaced by diesels in the 1950s. They were powered by 4-cylinder triple-expansion engines.

The belief that a steam boiler is a potentially explosive device is deep in the minds of an industrial community. There are even now those who, meeting a steam plant but never previously having seen one, ask first of all if it is about to explode. There is a reason for this: steam power went so far ahead of knowledge during the last century that explosions were frequent and disastrous. Coroner's juries sometimes accepted explanations which we now know to have been fallacious. The record is indeed a terrible one. In 1866 an engineer, one Mr E.R. Marten, reported on more than 1000 explosions which had killed more than 4000 people. Four years later, in 1870, he was to add 219 more explosions and 350 deaths. In North America things may not have been very different. One can read in Mark Twain harrowing accounts of explosions on Mississippi steam boats. Death by boiler explosion must have been familiar to the industrial people of the last century. Mr. Marten's thesis in his papers (*Proc. I. Mech. E.* 1866 & 1870) was that explosions were due to simple causes: structural weakness either original or acquired, defective safety valves or overheating of the metal plates. Indeed, in the examples with which Mr. Marten illustrates his papers structural weakness was high on the list. So far had boiler making outstripped knowledge. Added to this was misuse and lack of regular inspection.

The remedy was found in rational design, suitable materials and regular inspection. The insurance companies were to play a prominent part in boiler safety, which still depends on constant vigilance.

Enclosing the water-steam

A material such as mild steel can give its best performance when the structure into which it is built does not tend to change in shape when loads are applied. To resist internal pressure the best shape is a sphere, the next best is a long circular tube. A hollow structure which is to withstand external pressure is liable to an additional mode of failure. That is crumpling up or collapse as distinct from the tearing apart of the material.

Spherical boilers have been used but they have the disadvantage of minimum heating surface in comparison to their contents and any sediment derived from the feed water settles at the place where heat flow is most intense. This can lead to overheating and failure.

The advantages of water tube boilers were known from the eighteen-fifties onward, but for a very long time shell boilers dominated the thinking of engineers. By shell or tank boiler is meant a large metal container heated by furnaces within large tubes which pass through it. The furnace tubes were subject to external pressure and were thus limited in diameter, generally to something less than 1 m (3 ft). An advantage was that the sediment from the feed water could fall away from the intensely heated surfaces to the bottom of the shell where it could not do so much harm.

Disadvantages of the internal flue boiler are the nearness of the relatively cold surface to the fire and the unfavourable stressing conditions of the flue itself and of the flat parts of the outer shell. These were met by various types of support ring on the flue, and by stay bolts and angle gussets to help support the ends. Internal flue boilers were used for a very long time, indeed from early in the steam story, and they still have uses today. Advantages are tolerance to impure feed water and stability of working despite intermittent firing. There are many types of shell boiler for land use but the two-flue Lancashire boiler predominated. This was about 2.1 m (7 ft) in diameter and 8 m (26 ft) long. It was enclosed in a brickwork setting into which passages were built where further transfer of heat took place from the flue gases. For use at sea the Scotch marine boiler was dominant. Since brickwork setting was not appropriate, these boilers were of larger relative diameter and shorter length. They contained from one to four furnace tubes. Convective heat was also extracted in return tubes above the level of the furnaces. Diameters were up to 5 m (16.5 ft) and lengths up to 3 m (10 ft) for single ended boilers and twice this length for double ended. When diameter was limited an elongated form of the boiler was used. The flues discharged into a mid-length chamber whence fire tubes continued to an uptake at the end remote from the furnaces.

The author associates them, along with four-cylinder triple expansion engines, with the Liverpool-Birkenhead ferry when it was worked by steam.

Water-tube boilers

In the simplest form a water-tube boiler comprises an upper steam drum connected to a lower water (or *mud*) drum by a large number of water tubes which comprise the greater part of the heating surface. Their basic advantage is in the possibility of a large combustion chamber and reduced size and weight compared with a shell boiler. The reduced water content makes them more sensitive to rate of feeding and of firing. Indeed on some boilers the whole water content may be evaporated in a matter of minutes. The relatively small diameter of drums and tubes makes it possible to build them for high pressure.

The idea of tubular boilers is an old one but they were slow to become predominant. It was not unusual for Atlantic liners to use water tube boilers to drive the propulsion machinery at sea but to have one or two Scotch boilers for use in harbour. The rising flow in the tubes near to the furnace can be violent, projecting water and steam into the upper drum. This may call for more or less refined anti-priming devices. It is good practice to maintain circulation by having unheated downcomer pipes from the upper water space to the lower drum. This was not always done, with the result that stagnation of the water and local overheating could occur. The Field tube is a special case in which an inner concentric tube takes water down to the bottom of a heated blind-ended water tube. Evaporation in the annulus takes place with a violence which prevents deposition of sediment. Field tubes are associated with quick-steaming devices such as boilers used in the past in fire engines and currently in some steam launches.

Water-tube boilers have appeared in many different forms but those so far discussed, along with fire-tube boilers, depend on the maintenance of a fairly constant water level which is observed through a suitable glass gauge. Both types, shell and water-tube, can be classed as water level boilers.

Monotube boilers

In the monotube boiler water is pumped in almost continuously at one end of a coil of tubes and steam emerges at the other. The idea is at least 150 years old. The quantity of water is small, which means that the fire must respond very quickly to maintain control of temperature and pressure. These boilers developed rapidly during the days of steam automobiles and today, completely automated, they are widely used in industry, generally known as steam generators rather than by the older name of boiler.

The monotube in general is of small diameter tubing, hence it can have great strength. Also it contains but little water and so the hazards in the event of failure are reduced.

Small-scale monotube boilers

(1)   *Wet steam*

In these boilers water is pumped through the coil at a slightly greater rate than can be evaporated. The resultant wet steam is then passed through a mechanical separator. The dry component can be used directly in an engine or it can first be superheated. The water content returns to the hot well to be pumped round again. These boilers need no separate control of temperature since it corresponds to the pressure.

(2)   *Flash steam*

In this boiler the empty tube is maintained at a constant high temperature. When steam is required water is pumped in. This turns almost immediately into steam (is *flashed* into steam) to be used immediately in the engine. One method of control applicable to oil firing is to use coupled pumps, the amount of fuel delivered bearing a fixed relation to the amount of steam to be produced. Marine applications can often work at a steady rate of firing and water feed.

Small scale boilers today

At present the water-level boiler, either fire or water-tube, is much the most popular. Enthusiast users delight in acquiring the skills of boiler management of 150 years ago. This means constant observation of water and pressure levels with appropriate adjustments to the feed and fire conditions. Both water-tube and fire-tube types are popular. these boilers need constant vigilance in use and in maintenance and normally need to be subject to an annual inspection.

There is some use of flash boilers, often in conjunction with uniflow engines, and more use of wet-steam monotube boilers with ordinary steam engines. This seems to be more marked in North America than in Europe. The cost of a monotube boiler need only be a fraction of that of a water-level boiler and the hazard, in the event of mishandling, should be less. However, it needs a different technique in handling.

Isolated articles both for and against monotube boilers appear from time to time, but a solid body of published operating experience is still awaited.

Locomotive boilers

In the early eighteen-twenties, these were shell-type boilers with a single furnace tube. By 1830, very soon after the *Rocket*, the locomotive *Planet* was delivered by Robert Stephenson to the Liverpool and Manchester Railway. This locomotive set a pattern which has endured. It used a more or less rectangular water-walled fire box which fed its gaseous products into a single bank of fire tubes. These passed through a cylindrical shell to a front-end smoke box.

The structural problems arising from steam pressure being contained between flat surfaces was met by the use of a large number of surface-to-surface stay bolts. One hundred and fifty years of experience do not seem to have produced a better design which could be fitted into the space available on a locomotive engine. Heat transfer is undoubtedly helped by the surging of the water when the machine is on the road. A very similar type of boiler, but sometimes with a side fire-door instead of an end fire-door has had some application on the larger types of steam launch.

CHAPTER 6

Steam is set to Work

Floating Crane

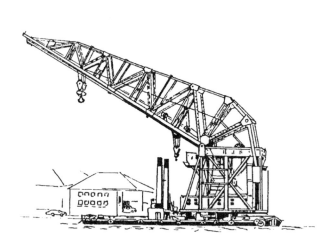

Steam floating cranes such as the Mammoth found constant employment in big seaports for both handling exceptional cargo and in ship building and repair. Their descendants can still be seen doing the same duties.

Steam jets

A steam nozzle is a form of engine in that a thermodynamic process can be completed there. Some of the random energy of the molecules and some of that manifested by the pressure at entry can be converted into the ordered flow of a moving stream at exit. Work is being done, but on the steam itself, not on a piston.

Some of the kinetic energy of a high velocity jet can be made to appear as shaft work in such a device as the primitive engine of Hero. In this the nozzle, by the principle of reaction, moves in the opposite direction from the jet. The process is similar to that of a jet-propelled aircraft. Alternatively, the jet can be deflected by a moving blade as the wind is by a windmill. The combination of jet and moving blade is a turbine.

The longitudinal profile of a hydraulic nozzle, or that of a fluid which is only slightly compressible, is simple. A nicely rounded entry followed by a uniform convergence is all that is required. This applies to the nozzle on a fireman's hose, for instance, or to the blast pipe on a locomotive (figure 6.1a). However, sometimes steam has to be expanded through a large ratio. Initially its compressibility can be neglected; finally its compressibility is dominant.

The jet throat

The net effect is that such a nozzle must first contract to a throat and then diverge to an extent depending on the back pressure. Such nozzles (figure 6.1b) are used in the injector and in some steam turbines. Accepted doctrine shows that at the throat the pressure has fallen to about 0.58 of the initial pressure and the velocity has attained the velocity of sound in steam. Further expansion then involves supersonic flow. The nozzle length must terminate when the velocity has reached a point corresponding to the back pressure.

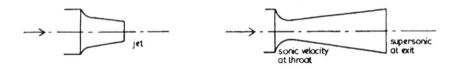

Figure 6.1

a) Converging Nozzle – blast pipe   *b) Converging-diverging Nozzle*

Steam jet velocities are high; 500 m/s (1120 miles/hr) is not unusual. Turbine blades which seek to use such jets must have a high velocity also. Hence the technological requirements are severe and they cannot really be included in simple steam applications. However, supersonic flow might well take place in an ordinary injector used for boiler feed.

The jet pump or ejector

The principle of one jet pump is met by most people in a school science laboratory where a device fitted to a water tap can produce suction. This is commonly used to speed up the flow through a filter. On an industrial scale jet pumps, often under the name of ejectors, have numerous applications. From an energy point of view, the efficiency is necessarily low, as indeed is any operation involving such an irreversible process as the mixing of two fluids with widely differing velocities. However, the absence of moving parts and the simplicity may compensate for this. The broad principles on which jet pumps work are clear enough, but the exact mechanism of their action is obscure.

A jet driven through a fluid at rest tends to entrain some of the surrounding fluid until ultimately a bigger mass is moving at a lower velocity. Entrainment follows from friction and tubulence at the interface.

Water jets are often used for moving water or air. The reverse process is not so effective, but air jets can be used satisfactorily for moving air.

Steam jets are rather special, since often the steam condenses into water during the process.

A common use on small steam boats is to use a steam-jet pump for clearing bilge water and another for drawing combustion air through the fire.

The injector

The injector (figure 6.2) is a device which uses steam to pump cold feed water into the boiler from which the steam itself has been derived. It does this without the aid of mechanically moving parts. It came quite early in locomotive history and is still widely used on locomotive and other boilers where for practical reasons cold feed water is likely to be used.

Although when it is in operation it is a steady-state flow process, understanding is helped by considering three separate stages in its action:

(a)   a steam-accelerating nozzle which will be of the converging diverging type to give supersonic flow,

(b)   the mixing and condensing stage, when cold feed water enters. The volume of the mixture is reduced but the momentum of the steam is conserved so that the mixture of feed water and condensate still moves with a high, but subsonic velocity,

(c)   the mixture flows into a diverging passage which (the flow being subsonic) slows it down (or acts as a diffuser) and increases the pressure sufficiently for it to enter the boiler.

The proportions of an injector are critical and normally, when being started in operation, an overflow is used until the jets become established. The

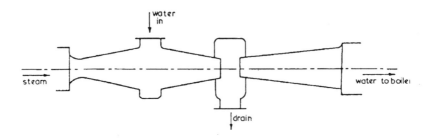

Figure 6.2
The Injector

principal disadvantage of the injector is its inability to use heated feed water, since this would not condense the steam in stage (b) above.

The continuity equation

A more formal statement of the flow in the nozzle is expressed by the equation of continuity. The statement that when conditions are steady then the rate at which steam enters a pump is the same as that at which it leaves is the basis of the far-reaching equation of continuity.

$$\text{In symbols,} \qquad m = \rho V A$$

m = mass flow rate (kg/s)
ρ = density (kg/m^3)
V = velocity (m/s)
A = cross-sectional area (m^2)

When ρ is a constant (or nearly so) as pressure falls, then as V increases, so A must diminish. This is the case with water or with the first part of a steam expansion.

When ρ is falling rapidly and V increasing slowly, then A must increase as well. This is the case after the throat of a nozzle when the flow has become supersonic.

It is well to point out that the shape of the passage which accelerates supersonic flow does exactly the opposite in the more ordinary subsonic state.

Those seeking to apply steam power in a small and simple way are only likely to meet supersonic flow in the steam nozzle of an injector.

The steam plant

The beginning stage of a power plant is the combustion of fuel. If the fuel is a solid (or a heavy oil) a high air velocity is needed to secure intense combustion. The draught necessary may be produced by a chimney stack (natural draught), by fans or by steam jets. Draught is considered to be either

(a)   induced, when air is sucked through the fire, or

(b)   forced, when air is forced through the fire.

The obvious case of induced draught is the factory chimney. As a means of draught production it is rather expensive. It takes a stack 140 ft high to lower the pressure over a fire by 1 inch water gauge, but the high stack does help to distribute the products of combustion over a wider area (and thus distribute pollution to more distant neighbours!).

The locomotive engine uses induced draught produced by a steam jet pump, being the blast pipe carrying the engine exhaust.

Forced draught has two main manifestations: (a) closed stokehold, and (b) closed ashpit. The closed stokehold system involves the whole boiler being under pressure (up to about 2 inches water gauge). This, however, does ensure some ventilation of a potentially very hot area.

The closed ashpit system (see figure 6.4) involves ducted high-pressure air to the space under the fire. It is potentially dangerous if a fire door is opened when the blast is on. Accordingly, the fire door latch is made to interlock with a valve that cuts off the air supply.

The 'puffer' power plant

The outstanding feature of this type of plant is the use of exhaust steam to blow the fire (figure 6.3). It is the simplest of all steam plants, and it is suitable where there is a ready supply of sufficiently clean water for the boiler, since there is no condensate to recycle. It is the plant which made the locomotive a practical machine and it remained predominant in this field so long as railway steam was important. It is also a practical system for small steam launches which work on fairly clean fresh water. A valuable property of the blast pipe is that it has a tendency towards self-regulation. An increased power demand means more steam and a more strongly blown fire.

Water can be fed into the boiler by either a mechanical feed pump or an injector. The injector has always been particularly favoured for locomotive work where it has the advantage of small size and weight. Marine plants, which have in general a much steadier load, tend to use a feed pump driven mechanically from the engine.

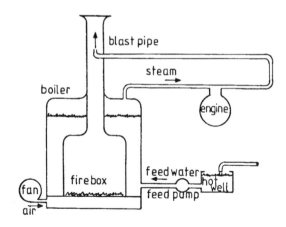

Figure 6.3
Puffer Steam Plant

The condensing steam plant

After leaving the engine the steam is condensed back to water and is normally re-used as feed for the engine. Thus the same clean water can be used over and over again (figure 6.4). This is of advantage in a sea-going plant since it avoids an accumulation of salt in the boiler. It may also be desirable for water conservation in arid lands.

Apart from cleanliness and conservation, condensation at a lower pressure than than that of the atmosphere gives a bigger pressure drop across the engine and thus can make more work available on the engine shaft. However, this extra work must be offset against the increased mechanical complication involved. Generally, the larger the plant the greater the gain from a low-pressure exhaust.

On the small scale, extra parasitic losses may render increased expansion less worth while. These losses are:

(a)   work required for the condenser extraction pump;

(b)   work required for the furnace blower in the absence of exhaust blast;

(c)   work required for a condenser cooling water circulating pump.

On very small marine craft, the use of a keel condenser may remove the need for a cooling water pump.

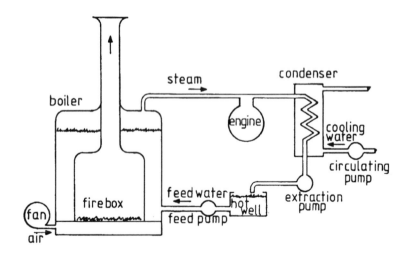

Figure 6.4
Feed Water Cycle

Miscellaneous modifications to the simple plant layout

Superheating

A superheating coil between the boiler and the engine often improves output and economy. Superheaters nowadays are often incorporated in the boiler, but formerly for greater control were sometimes separately fired. However, superheated steam brings with it the need for cylinder lubrication. Many engines have depended for cylinder lubrication entirely on the water component of the wet steam and have run very well. The great reciprocators of the Atlantic liners (which lasted well into the 1930s) often used wet steam and no cylinder oil. Cylinder oil is disadvantageous in a marine plant. The oil needs to be completely filtered out before the water gets back to the boiler.

Feed water heating

Feed heating is always valuable from an economy point of view. Two methods are available. One uses waste heat from the exhaust steam (acting perhaps as the first stage of a surface condenser). The other uses heat in the chimney stack where the gases have fallen to too low a temperature to be of use in the boiler. These stack heaters are called economizers.

Combustion air heating

If air to be used for combustion can first have its temperature increased, further economy is possible. After the flue gases have given up some heat in the economiser there may still be some available for air heating.

CHAPTER 7

Steam in the Cylinder

Crofton Canal Pumping Station

Before this pumping station was closed down overall tests were organised by Mr K.W. Willans for the Newcomen Society. The sketch shows the temporary weir which was built to measure the water flow from the pumps. The pumping station has since been restored by voluntary effort.

The indicator

Early, very early, in the history of the steam engine there arose a need to know what the steam did as it expanded in the cylinder. The problem was attacked by James Watt who made a device and kept it secret. Briefly, a pencil was mounted on the rod of a spring-controlled piston. This went up and down as the pressure in the engine cylinder varied. At the same time a sliding board was oscillated in time with the strokes of the engine. Combining these effects by pressing the pencil onto a paper clipped to the board gave a graph representing pressure plotted against piston stroke. Measurements from this graph, together with the dimensions of the engine and its speed enabled the power being developed on the engine piston to be calculated. The apparatus was known as an engine indicator and the record it drew on the board was the indicator diagram. Over the century which followed the indicator became a more and more refined piece of apparatus. It probably developed as far as a mechanical device (which cannot avoid some friction and inertia) could reasonably go. Although the indicator diagram can never be proved to be true, it can in skilled hands give consistent information. It was an essential tool in engine development and an aid in technical education. It is often convenient to change the scale of the piston stroke to one of piston swept volume. The area enclosed be the indicator diagram is then a measure of the work done on the piston.

The hypothetical indicator diagram

A hypothetical indicator diagram is one which is assumed for an imaginary engine where steam can flow without restriction or leakage.

Consideration of the hypothetical diagram is the first stage in the design of an engine which has to meet specific requirements of power, speed and steam conditions. Such a diagram is sketched in figure 7.1. Four cardinal points are apparent which correspond to the opening and closing of the cylinder to inlet and exhaust respectively. These points are: Admission at A and cut-off at B on the steam side, Release at C and compression at D on the exhaust side. Cut off at B before the end of the stroke enables extra work to be done by a given quantity of steam. Compression at D before the end of the stroke is of value thermodynamically, in that the pressure is raised nearer to that of the inlet before fresh steam is admitted, and mechanically in that the pressure of the steam on the piston helps to slow it down as it nears the end of its stroke. This reduces the cyclical load on the bearings and is called cushioning. Work done in the compression process can be largely restored during the subsequent re-expansion with little net loss.

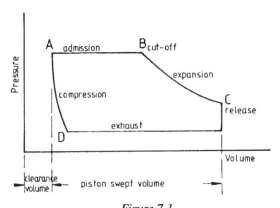

Figure 7.1

Hypothetical Indicator Diagram

Clearance volume is the space between the piston and the cylinder head at the end of the stroke. Ideally, this should be such that the pressure at the end of the stroke is near to that of the steam supply. The fresh steam can then enter without too much turbulence. The clearance volume depends much on the exhaust pressure. An engine working a 7 bar (100 lbf/in²) with atmospheric exhaust could advantageously use a clearance volume of about one seventh of the piston swept volume. An engine exhausting into a low-pressure condenser would need a much smaller clearance if it is to make effective use of compression.

An engine's *Expansion Ratio* is defined as

$$\frac{piston\ swept\ volume\ +\ clearance\ volume}{volume\ at\ cut\ off\ +\ clearance\ volume}$$

Mean effective pressure

The difference between the average pressure on the piston during the power stroke and that on the return stroke is called the *mean effective pressure* (M.E.P.). This can be readily calculated from the dimensions of the indicator diagram.

Diagram factor

Since valves do not open and close instantaneously and since steam is subject to inertia and friction, the hypothetical diagram cannot be attained. The real diagram must lie within the hypothetical diagram and it has all its corners rounded off. The area of the real diagram expressed as a fraction of the hypothetical is called the *diagram factor*. A realistic diagram factor may be about 0.7.

Powers

The mean effective pressure combined with the engine dimensions and speed gives a means of calculating the power which is being developed on the piston of an engine. Such powers are known as indicated (horse-)powers (I.H.P.). This was the only power measurement ever made on most big engines.

The power which an engine delivers to its shaft may be measured. Since such powers, if measured at all, were generally measured by a brake, they are called the brake horsepower or the shaft power. The difference between indicated and brake power is that which is lost by friction within the engine, and the power needed for its essential auxiliaries (feed pumps, extraction pumps, etc.).

The ratio of shaft power to indicated power is the mechanical efficiency.

The mechanical efficiency of an engine depends much on the loading and on the speed. The author has measured values in excess of 0.9 for a low-pressure non- condensing engine on full load, and as low as 0.6 for a high-speed oil engine, also on full load.

The concept of mechanical efficiency is important on small engines where friction losses are relatively large. Factors which undoubtedly improve the indicated power may so much increase the friction as to reduce the power available on the shaft.

Over expansion – the negative loop

An engine necessarily works against a back pressure which, in a simple case, may be that of the atmosphere. The inevitable friction within the engine may be considered as an increment in the back pressure applied to a frictionless engine. If an engine working on a low pressure has too early a cut off, expansion may take place to a pressure below that of the effective back pressure and work has to be drawn from the shaft to pump the steam out of the cylinder. Such a process is shown on an indicator diagram by a negative loop (figure 7.2). Negative loops can also occur at the start of the piston stroke, particularly so in engines controlled by a Stephenson link near to mid gear.

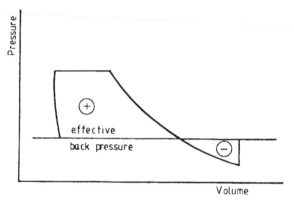

Figure 7.2

Indicator Diagram Showing Negative Loop

Brake mean effective pressure

The concept of mean effective pressure is so very useful that an artificial figure is sometimes introduced for engines which cannot be "indicated" but which can have their power measured on a brake. This is the brake mean effective pressure. It is found by equating the brake power to the expression derived for indicated power.

Calculation of indicated power

If

P = Mean effective pressure (measured from the indicator diagram)

L = Piston stroke

A = Piston area

N = Number of working strokes in unit time (not necessarily the same as revolutions)

then the indicated power is given by $PLAN$

In Standard International Units

P is in newtons/metre^2 (N/m^2)

L is in metres (m)

A is in metres^2 (m^2)

N is in working strokes/second (s^{-1})

and the power is in *watts (W)*.

In the old units

P is in lbf/in^2

L is in feet

A is in in^2

N is in working strokes/min

and the horse power is given by $\dfrac{PLAN}{33000}$

The brake mean effective pressure is then given by

$$B.M.E.P = \frac{33000 \times Brake\ Horse\ Power}{LAN}$$

"The Professors"

No subject can have grown so quickly from such a limited start as did mechanical engineering in the first half of the last century. In much engineering work there was no scientific guidance. Thermodynamic principles had not even been formulated, let alone appreciated at factory level. The materials available, cast iron, wrought iron and copper, were often quite unequal to the tasks expected of them and manufacturing methods and plant were rudimentary. Mineral oils were yet to come. Under such conditions the reciprocating steam engine reached the useful form much as we know it today. It was essentially the era of the practical man but some could see further. During the latter half of the nineteenth century the universities began to realise that engineering was a fit subject for scientific study. Professors were appointed at some provincial universities, their Chairs often endowed by merchants and shipowners. The contribution of these early professors was very significant indeed. One need only recall such names as Rankine, the Thomson brothers James and William (the latter to become Lord Kelvin), Osborne Reynolds, Unwin, Dalby, Ewing and Hele-Shaw to realise how great a contribution was to be made by the new engineering departments in the universities. (Alas, the new knowledge was often slow to reach manufacturing industry.) Engineering was much more to do with engines then and many of the new professors commissioned experimental engines to be made by local builders. These were adapted for research and teaching, using instrumentation of their own devising. Generally these engines were fairly large and of low speed. This made instrumentation more straightforward and the dimensions were realistic from an instructional point of view.

The "missing quantity"

Characteristic of the kind of investigations at this time was the derivation of the steam used per stroke from a point after the cut-off on the indicator diagram. Pressure and volume could be measured; hence knowing the specific volume of the steam from the steam tables, the mass used per stroke could be determined. The engine also had a surface condenser, so the steam used per stroke could also be calculated from the mass of condensate collected. When compared, the figure from the condensate was always much greater, up to about 30 percent, than that indicated. The difference was called the missing quantity – steam known to be passing through the engine but not giving evidence of its presence.

The hypothesis of initial condensation

The fact that Watt had improved the economy of the steam engine by moving the condensation process away from the working cylinder to a separate vessel was still in the minds of engineers, and the idea was extended to assume a rhythmic heating of the cylinder passages by the hot steam on entry, to be followed by a cooling by the slightly lower temperature steam on exhaust. A part of the fresh steam, it was argued, must condense on entry, to be re-evaporated as the pressure fell. The hypothesis seemed to fit the facts. Over the years it passed from doctrine to dogma, to exist as long as the reciprocating steam engine had a part in technical education. It is now realised that increasing wetness is inevitable in anything like a resisted expansion. This condensation can pass directly to exhaust, escaping as a water film under the slide valve and past the piston rings. This is sufficient to account for the missing quantity. The absence of leakage steam to exhaust when the engine is at rest is to be expected. It is the lubricating film of water which forms under the valve and piston rings when they are in motion which conveys the mass flow. This is hidden in a double acting engine, but very apparent in a single-acting piston engine.

The increase in wetness during expansion is demonstrated in Chapter 15 on Entropy. The problem also arises in steam turbines. The higher the initial pressure the wetter is the expanded steam. In steam turbines water particles can, by erosion, damage the turbine blades.

CHAPTER 8

Steam Leaves the Cylinder – Condensers

Bobbin Mill, Stott Park, Cumbria

This mill supplied bobbins to the textile industries of the North of England. Power was supplied by a water turbine and a single cylinder steam engine. The fuel was waste wood from the process. When electric supplies became available both water and steam were abandoned, but the consequent accumulation of wood waste continued. The mill has now been restored as an industrial museum.

The extent of the problem

Exhaust steam carries a considerable amount of energy and since it has become too degraded for significant power production it is normally rejected as waste. The extent of the energy rejection varies from somewhere near 70% for very large power stations up to about 98% for a small practical size of plant. Railway locomotives often rejected about 95% of the energy input, although better figures have been obtained under test conditions. A model steam engine only converts about 1% of the energy supplied!

Ideally this low grade energy should be used for low grade purposes, and to some extent it is. Hospitals and hotels are typical cases which require a moderate amount of power and a lot of heat. Certain industrial processes, such as paper making, have often combined power production with process heating. Ultimately, if ever fuel economy has to be taken seriously, this kind of system is inevitable.

However, most small plants just get rid of exhaust steam as best they can. The locomotive uses a little of the work capacity remaining in the steam to produce a chimney blast and hence the draught through the fire. In other plants some exhaust steam may be used to warm the feed water between the feed pump and the boiler. This may bring about a 10% economy in fuel, e.g. raising a small plant's efficiency from about 5% to about 5.5%.

Condensation

Exhaust steam may be condensed back to water for any or all of the following reasons:

(1)   to reduce the nuisance value of the steam discharge,

(2)   to conserve clean water in order to use it again,

(3)   to achieve a bigger pressure and temperature drop across the engine and therefore to increase its power and perhaps its economy.

Condensers fall into two main classes, surface condensers where a metal surface separates the condensate from the cooling medium, or mixing condensers where cold water is sprayed into the exhaust steam.

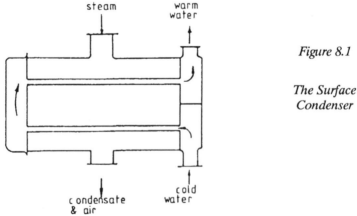

Figure 8.1

The Surface Condenser

The surface condenser

The cooling medium for a surface condenser may be either air or water. Air condensers are associated with steam vehicles. A condenser reduces the size of tank which a road vehicle has to carry and in some cases it has helped steam locomotives to operate in arid lands. Formerly they were also associated with very small steam plants used in urban areas. In this case they were often mounted on a roof. The effectiveness of such condensers can be increased if a small amount of water is allowed to trickle over them. This is the evaporative condenser. It might not, on balance, conserve much water, but it might enable a less pure source to be used for cooling.

Surface condensers using water for a cooling medium nowadays pump the cooling water through banks of copper alloy tubes which pass through a closed iron or steel container (figure 8.1). The exhaust steam comes into contact with the tubes where it is condensed and it is drawn away at the bottom of the container. Surface condensers are used for practically all significant power plants.

The keel condenser

Small steam craft may advantageously use a keel condenser. This is a length of copper pipe alongside the keel. The cooling water circulating pump is eliminated and no space is taken up inside the boat. While such devices are most effective on a small scale, they would be too vulnerable to use on a sea-going ship.

The mixing condenser

In these condensers the cooling water as a jet or spray comes into contact with the steam being condensed. They date from the very earliest days of steam power and remained in significant use for as long as large, low-speed factory engines existed. The common type was generally known as the jet condenser. It could be better described as a spray condenser (figure 8.2).

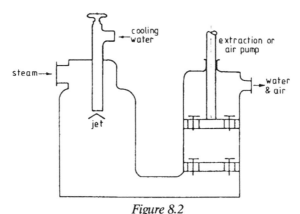

Figure 8.2

The Jet Condenser

Characteristically in a factory area the cooling water came from a mill dam or lodge or, if appropriate, from a canal. A story published in the proceedings of a learned society is worth repeating. A factory fireman, being taken to task for failing to maintain an adequate pressure of steam, explained that there were so many factories using the canal that all the steam had been boiled out of the water before it reached him! Jet condensers were used at sea for a while until surface condensers were satisfactory, even though it meant frequent boiler blowdown to remove salt deposits. They are still in use on the rebuilt steamer *Segwun* which works on Lake Muskoka in Ontario. The water there is of great purity.

The ejector condenser

The ejector condenser is a hydraulic device which combines the functions of condensation and extraction. A hydraulically operated jet pump extracted both steam and air. The steam was condensed and the mixture passed into a diverging passage which built up its pressure to atmospheric. The device could produce a high degree of vacuum, but unless a pressure water supply was available one had to be produced at the expense of engine power.

An ejector condenser known to the author lies in a textile bobbin mill at Stott Park in Cumbria. The mill was formerly driven by water power supplemented by a steam plant working off the wood waste. A small amount of water was diverted from the turbine reservoir to supply the condenser. Another reported to the author was on an inland steam launch. Here a pump was necessary to drive the jet.

An example set up on an experimental rig revealed a potential danger. Inadvertently, prior to shutting down the condenser, water was turned off before the steam was turned off the engine. This caused a reflux of water into the cylinder which had a profound effect on the mechanical integrity of the engine.

The extraction pump

If condensation is used to secure a low pressure region for the engine to exhaust into, the condensate will have to be pumped out of the condenser. However, it is not only water which is found in the condenser. Air is present as well. This has been dissolved in the feed water and comes over with the steam, or it may be due to inward leakage into the low pressure parts of the plant. If this is not removed it rapidly destroys the vacuum. Hence both air and water have to be constantly pumped out of the condenser. The air is at a low partial pressure and has a large volume. If the same pump is used for air and water it has to be designed with air in mind. Consequently it is called the air pump even though it may deal with water as well. On significant plants, the two functions of air and water extraction are now separated. Steam jet pumps in series are often used for the first stage of air extraction. Quite separate pumps are used for the water.

Compression condensing

A mixture of steam and water can behave in an apparently anomalous manner. if the mixture is only slightly wet, compression would dry it, but if it is very wet, compression turns it all to liquid. Attempts have been made to use this as an aid to the increasing of a steam cycle efficiency but apparently the possible gains have been outweighed by the extra complication of the mechanical losses in the compression.

Fifty years ago experiments were made on a railway locomotive and they were evidently encouraging for they were continued after World War II, but only until the general abandonment of railway steam.

Regenerative condensers

A surface condenser always involves an inner contradiction. Air in the condenser is at a low partial pressure, and hence it has a large volume. To reduce air pump size (and power) the air should be cooled as much as possible. However the condensate should only have its latent heat removed since further cooling is waste. The problem is tackled in various ways, such as arranging for the air to be drawn through the coldest bank of tubes and by encouraging the condensate to rain down through the entering steam before it reaches the extraction pump.

CHAPTER 9

On Matters Mechanical

RMS Adriatic
The largest of the four White Star ships which maintained the Liverpool – North America service. Sketched from a photograph taken on her last passenger-carrying voyage, when, as a cruising liner, she called at Funchal in 1933

The 'ordinary' steam engine

Such steam engines as are found in use today are likely to be double-acting with steam controlled by a simple slide valve. This in turn is operated by an eccentric. It is the form of engine developed for the railway locomotive, later adapted for marine use. For half a century it was the normal engine used for small workshop applications. The great mill engines followed quite a different line of development which has died with them. Although some small engines were of refined and of precise construction, others of local build showed quite primitive construction, owing more to the forge than to the lathe. Yet they worked, depending much on their generous clearances.

The engine owed a lot to the properties of the flat slide valve. To some extent this could act as a relief if water got into the cylinder, and it was self-compensating for wear. However it was suited best to moderate pressures and temperatures. The flat slide valve depends on a film of fluid lubrication (generally the water component of the wet steam): without this it can become quite locked up. Even with it, it is known that the valve absorbs a measurable amount of power (in terms of the engine output). This is partly indicated by the size of the rods required to drive it. Large valves often use spring-loaded relief frames to exclude high pressure steam from the back of the valve.

The piston type of slide valve is altogether more refined. It requires more precise construction and needs rings, or honed surfaces, to make it steam tight. It is relatively easy to drive but its small clearances need clean steam and it is without the relief valve properties of the flat valve.

The slide valve

Early engines evidently used a valve which just covered the ports when the valve was in the mid-position (see figure 9.1). Since the piston was about to start its stroke the eccentric was set at 90° in advance of the crank. Expansive working was impossible and the hypothetical indicator diagram was a rectangle.

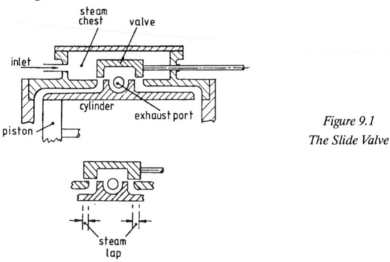

Figure 9.1

The Slide Valve

Steam lap

To secure expansive working, the valve must be made to overlap the ports in order that part of its movement takes place with the port closed to steam. However, so that the valve still opens to steam at the correct piston position the eccentric must be advanced in excess of the essential 90°. The amount by which the valve overlaps the port when it is in its mid-position is called the steam lap (figure 9.1).

Steam lead

It may be desired to have the valve very slightly open to steam at the start of the piston stroke. In a high speed engine this enables the pressure to be built up behind the piston before motion begins. Alternatively, on small single cylinder reversing engines (as used on boats) some owners prefer to use a negative lead. When the flywheel needs to be manhandled near the dead centre it is then less likely to kick back in the wrong direction.

The angle of advance

The angle of advance is the angle through which the eccentric must be advanced (in excess of 90°) to bring the valve to the desired position, taking into account both lap and lead, when the piston is at the extremity of its stroke.

Steam lap and lead and angle of advance define the points of admission and cut-off. Corresponding laps can exist on the exhaust side of the valve which define points of release and compression, but they are not always used. These definitions apply to the piston valve exactly as they do to the flat valve.

Inside and outside admission

When a piston valve is used the steam supply can either be between the two piston components of the valve, or it may be at the ends with the exhaust in the middle. The two states are known as inside and outside admission respectively. When the valve has neither lap nor lead a simple and much used reversing facility is obtained by interchanging the inlet and exhaust connections. The same is sometimes done with flat valves, but this requires that the back of the valve shall slide closely against the steam chest cover. Otherwise it could be lifted off its seat when inside admission is used.

Double action

The accepted form of engine in which the steam acts alternately on opposite sides of the piston follows directly from the requirements of the locomotive for compactness and easy starting. In due course it proved almost equally desirable for the marine engine but it was not without its drawbacks. This was realized well enough ninety years ago when developments were strongly in the direction of the single-acting engine. However, engine development slowed down before the challenge of the internal combustion engine and steam turbine. Surviving engines with their open and easily understood linkwork can have a strong emotional appeal, suggesting a more leisured age in which people had time to stand and stare. (Perhaps this was so for the owner of a varnished teak steam launch, but not so much for the tug- or barge-hand!)

The disadvantages of double-action stem from alternating forces in the rods. These tend towards metal fatigue (fractured rods are not unknown today) and from difficulties in the lubrication of a bearing subjected to continually reversing loads. The lubrication of the connecting rod bearings is notoriously difficult.

(Double-action in large, low-speed, internal combustion engines has been used to some extent in marine diesels, but it has never been really popular or made much headway in internal combustion engines.)

When a lubricated bearing supports a steady load it is well established that the shaft takes up a slightly eccentric position within the bearing (figure 9.2). An oil film in the region of maximum clearance and lowest pressure is continually being dragged by the mechanism of viscosity into the region where the pressure is high. It is the oil film which supports the load without any metal to metal contact. Such a bearing, when conditions are ideal, works for extremely long periods, almost indefinitely, without measurable wear. Anything which interrupts the continuity of the oil film is detrimental. (The author has on occasion completely cured a hot bearing by soldering up the oil grooves!) When the load is alternating in direction this steady film never has a chance to form, and lubrication depends on a greasy film which incompletely clings to the surface of the metal. The small end of the connecting rod is the most difficult of the lubrication problems. As well as reversed loading it never undergoes complete rotation and so continuous film lubrication is not established. These difficulties can be overcome by pressure oil supply, but this may be unacceptable in an open crank engine.

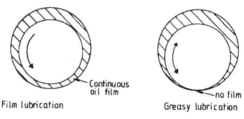

Figure 9.2

The Hydrodynamic Bearing

Piston leakage

Double-action has one real advantage, however, in that it conceals piston leakage and so reduces mess around the engine. In all single-acting steam engine experiments which the author has conducted or witnessed, the amount of water passing the piston has been impressive, even in engines of highest quality and accurate machining. Water film on the cylinder wall passes readily as the piston rings glide over it. (The test of putting pressure on a stalled engine and observing no blow-by does not tell the whole story.) Such steam engines as use splash lubrication normally have a layer of oil floating on top of a sump full of water. Excess water is removed by a submerged weir. All this was realised well enough one hundred years ago when single-acting engines normally used a closed crank case.

Poppet valves

The eccentric driven slide valve does not lend itself to rapid action and hence an early cut-off, nor does it lend itself to extreme temperatures. In these circumstances though, the cam operated poppet valve (perhaps double-beat) can be used with advantage.

Single action

Peter Willans was one of the most innovative of Victorian steam engineers. He must have had practical experience of fatigue and wear problems, for very little work had been published when, in 1874 at the age of 22, he patented his first steam engine. This, a simple expansion marine engine, was a three-cylinder, single-acting, closed crankcase design. A downward extension of the piston was shaped so as to act as a piston valve for the cylinder which was 120° behind. Reversing was by a six-port, two-way cock. This changed the sequence and so reversed the engine. His concept was of unparalleled simplicity. However, it needed a precision of manufacture which was then unusual. This precision led him on to the concept of interchangeable parts for use in his engine. Other manufacturers took up the single-action concept and it was really going ahead when innovative steam reciprocating engineering ceased before the challenge of the internal combustion engine and the steam turbine.

Two ocean steamships

In 1932 the author served briefly as a supernumerary engineer on the Elder Dempster liner *Appam* and in 1933 on the White Star liner *Adriatic*. This was on the last passenger voyage the latter was to make. These ships were passenger liners built early in the century by Harland and Wolff. Apart from differences in size and speed, they had much in common. Both used coal-fired Scotch Marine boilers. Steam was raised at 215 lb/in^2. This was used without superheat in quadruple expansion engines. The increase in power and improvement in economy that superheat could bring was well known, but troubles which could follow from cylinder lubrication made it generally unacceptable at sea.

Steam was reduced in pressure to 160 lb/in^2 for the electrical generator and to 100 lb/in^2 for all the other auxiliaries. Auxiliary exhaust went into a heating main at positive pressure. Excess went into the main condenser when at sea or into an auxiliary condenser when in port.

Apart from the condenser cooling water pumps which were centrifugal, nearly all auxiliary pumps were direct-acting, either of the shuttle valve or of the duplex type. Pumps were numerous; boiler feed, condenser extraction, bilge, ballast and firefighting, also sanitation, deck washing, fresh water and ash ejection. While all were independent, a complex system of cross connections existed which could be used in emergency.

Deck machinery, also steam driven and perhaps three hundred feet from the boiler room, included the anchor winch, fore and aft mooring winches, lifeboat and cargo winches and, most important of all, the steering engine. (Steam steering engines justify a special description which is given later in this chapter.)

Everything was under manual control. Water gauge glasses were continually observed and check valves, feed pumps or boiler draught were regulated accordingly. Steam engine rooms were very hot and a sweat rag was issued at the start of a watch. This was rigorously checked in at the end. (A rag in the bilge nearly sank one of Scott's Antarctic ships.) Each engineer carried a wheel spanner polished from constant use. This device hooked over a hot valve wheel when adjustments had to be made. All significant bearings had a cooling water service. In some cases permanent nozzles were arranged which in case of need could spray cold water over them. Eccentrics and thrust collars worked in troughs of oil-water emulsion. Bearing temperatures were sensed by hand. The watch keepers, by careful timing, would feel the big ends as they hurtled around. At half hour intervals all the thrust blocks and the bearings of the propeller shafts in the tunnels would be checked. At the same time, the inward leakage of sea water through the stern tube glands would be verified. This was necessary for the lubrication of the lignum vitae bearings. Fresh water was constantly made in the evaporator. This was a low pressure boiler, heated by auxiliary steam which then discharged into the main condenser. It drew its feed, slightly warmed, from the main condenser cooling water discharge.

Steering engines

Steam was first applied to the steering of a ship on the *Great Eastern*, and the date was 1867, when she had become a cable layer. Prior to the use of steam, up to one hundred men were needed to steer a large ship under extreme conditions. The work was arduous and dangerous. Wave pressure on the rudder could fling men over the steering wheel. Steering engines were of the rather uneconomic type which had neither lap nor lead and which were capable of either outside or inside admission to the slide valve. The valve was preferably of the piston type but not necessarily so. Flat slide valves held down by the cover of the valve chest are recorded. Steering engines remained practically unchanged in principle as long as steam ships were dominant on the high seas. The engines were two-cylinder double-acting with cranks at 90°. They were supplied from a distributing valve (which might be identical to the engine valves). When the steering wheel was turned the distributing valve was displaced in the appropriate direction. Immediately the engine would start and in turn drive a feedback mechanism which tended to close the valve. Thus the engine turned only as long as the steering wheel turned, and at a corresponding speed. Similarly, it stopped and reversed whenever the steering wheel stopped and reversed.

The *Great Eastern* steering engine had generous cylinder clearance and no provision for cylinder drainage other than gravity. The designer claimed that the engine could, if need be, run on water (perhaps prophetic, since most steering engines are today hydraulically driven, albeit by oil). It was designed to work at 20 lb/in^2 but was still effective when the pressure was 8 lb/in^2. The basic control was a form of differential gear in that it responded to a difference in speed between the steering wheel and the steering engine. The anchor winch and boat deck winches also used this simple port changing method for reverse, but the cargo winches often used a Stephenson link.

The rotary engine

This refers to positive displacement engines and not to turbines, which move on quite different principles.

For some applications and to some inventors, the connecting rod and crank mechanism has seemed to be an unnecessary adjunct in a machine designed to turn fluid pressure into shaft work. Hence the positive displacement rotary engine (or pump). Often they are based on a drum which rotates eccentrically within a cylindrical casing. From the drum hinged, sliding or elastic vanes make contact with the casing. Another set of machines consists of pairs of lobes geared together which can cause a pressure change in the fluid which passes through them.

The idea is an old one. One of the founder members of the Institution of Mechanical Engineers apparently proposed such an engine and thereby attracted the wrath of the President himself, George Stephenson. He would clearly have none of it and could see no good in such a thing.

The idea persisted but apparently made little headway as an engine. When reversed and used as a low-pressure air compressor, such machines were widely used as furnace and forge blowers.

In the last forty years positive displacement rotary motors have had success in the field of oil hydraulics. The technology of oil machines is better than anything that was available to the early steam engineers and, by definition, problems of lubrication do not arise. The author has briefly operated a sliding vane oil machine as a steam engine. It certainly went round and gave reasonable power but it was noisy and it did not attract further experiments. A positive advantage was instant reversing by port changing and instant starting from cold on either steam or steam and water mixture. These machines may be more expensive to build than a simple piston and cylinder device and the sealing of the vanes tends to be an intractable problem. The rotary engine in fact, has been described (rather paradoxically in view of the above) as 'one of the great non-starters in the history of engineering' (Plint, *SIMEC* No.1 1971).

CHAPTER 10

Compounding and Uniflow

Traction Engines

Steam traction engines used for threshing were not uncommon in the 1920s. The specialised fairground engine also drove a dynamo for lighting and for driving a roundabout. These engines were elaborately decorated and beautifully maintained and to some were more attractive than the fair itself.

Compound expansion: general

The practice of compound expansion, or that of dividing the pressure drop among two or more cylinders, can be considered almost as old as the steam engine itself. Hornblower used a two-stage engine with condensation taking place in the low-pressure cylinder. Watt regarded the high pressure cylinder as a breach of his patent in that it used a separate condenser. During the first half of the nineteenth century expanding factories found themselves short of engine power, and so the practice of increasing the pressure and the speed of the initially primitive beam engines began. This led to breakages and explosions to an extent, to quote a contemporary engineer Fairbairn, 'that was ruinous to life and property'. However Fairbairn hastens to add that he did not mean to blame any one person in his attempts to increase the power of his steam engine to meet the demands of his mill. A more rational attempt was to build a higher pressure boiler which supplied a high-pressure engine geared to the same shafting as the original beam engine. The exhaust from this engine in turn drove the original engine of the mill. These supplementary engines were called *thrutchers*. A more economical approach, called the *McNaughting*, put the high pressure cylinder in a position were it could work on the beam of the original engine. Generally it was installed between the pivot and the connecting rod. here it could positively reduce the bending moment on the beam while still increasing the power of the engine.

These attempts were only meant to increase the power of the mill. It is tempting and plausible to suggest that someone noticed that, as well as increasing the power, they often increased the economy. However, this increase in economy came to the notice of shipowners who were ever desirous of sending their ships on longer and longer voyages without having to depend on bunkers laid by sailing ships. Early compound engines often had the high-pressure cylinder in tandem with the low-pressure on a single rod; this configuration was used both on land and at sea. Later in marine practice they were often on separate cranks, a practice which brings other advantages.

That the breaking up of the expansion into a number of separate stages could in some cases lead to an improved economy soon became accepted. Even if it had not improved the economy, there were sufficient practical advantages to warrant it. But why did it improve the economy? The theory of initial condensation was dragged out again, suggesting that lower temperature differences per stage would lead to less condensation. It all seemed to fit up to a point. To some extent it is quoted today. Experiments to support the theory included the use of steam jackets to keep the cylinder hot. Some experiments suggested that further economy could thus be secured; others did not, and the practice died out.

One reason for the improved economy of a compound engine may be sufficient. That is that compounding is likely to be accompanied by an increase in the ratio of expansion.

The hypothetical indicator card of a compound engine is represented by figure 10.1.

Neglecting clearance volume, the ratio of expansion is

$$\frac{Volume\ of\ LP}{Volume\ of\ HP\ at\ cut\text{-}off}$$

At H.P. release there is an irreversible pressure drop down to L.P. inlet pressure. This is not completely lost energy; some but not all can be recovered by the drying effect.

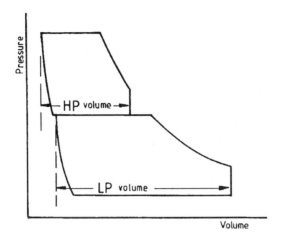

Figure 10.1

Hypothetical Indicator Diagram for a Compound Engine

The total power of the engine can only be influenced by the initial pressure or by the H.P. cut-off. Variations in L.P. cut-off control influence the power distribution between the cylinders. A later L.P. cut-off reduces L.P. power. For a normal condition a cylinder volume ratio of four (diameter ratio of two) is generally assumed to give approximately equal power per cylinder. When traditional small engines are found with a ratio differing much from this, one suspects that the manufacturer might have had an existing H.P. foundry pattern which came in useful!

Receiver heating

If a multi-cylinder engine is arranged for approximately equal work per cylinder, it follows that the smaller cylinders must work with the bigger pressure drop. This means that, starting with approximately dry steam, if the expansion in the high pressure cylinder is reasonably efficient, the steam will be wet as it enters the first receiver (this is demonstrated in Chapter 15 on Entropy). If some spare heat is available to dry the steam partially in the receiver then an overall increase in engine power can be expected.

This is not in accordance with the rigorous requirements of the Carnot cycle which requires that all heat must enter at the highest temperature. It should be regarded as on of the many compromises which an engineer has to make on account of the limitations of materials.

A boiler superheater may safely raise steam to a higher temperature than the engine cylinder can accept. The boiler steam can be passed through a heat interchanger in the first receiver, thereby drying the H.P. exhaust a little and making its operation in the next cylinder more effective.

Such an engine may have a delayed manœuvring response because of the increased volume of steam downstream of the stop valve.

Advantages of compound expansion

A large ratio of expansion can be obtained with a simple eccentric/slide valve combination. This may be a sufficient explanation for any improved economy which is observed.

By spreading the power among two or more cranks better balance and more uniform torque can be achieved. Dead-centre difficulties can then be overcome by the use of by-pass steam.

Lighter scantlings can be used since the highest pressure is confined to the smallest cylinder.

Low pressure differences enable flat slide valves to be used, particularly in the L.P. cylinder.

Over-expansion

Compound engines may have problems which a simple engine would be able to suppress. These can arise when two-crank engines are throttled down to work at very low load and speed. The high-pressure cylinder may then take more than its fair share of the load. If indicator cards could be taken, a pronounced negative loop would be shown in the low-pressure diagram. In other words, the high-pressure cylinder would have to supply work to overcome friction in the low-pressure cylinder and to pump out the over-expanded steam. Symptoms may be low-pressure crosshead "slop" – when the rod is pulling on the crosshead instead of pushing or vice-versa, erratic running or even abrupt stalling. The symptoms are well recorded.

The problem stems from lack of match between the engine and the load and it raises the question as to whether or not compound expansion is justified in the particular case. If the mismatch is not too severe a remedy may be sought in changes in the valve events, so as to reduce the ratio of expansion. This may mean changes in lap, lead and angle of advance. Alternatively, a fairly heavy flywheel may be able to suppress the symptoms.

Compound versus simple

When we read their contributions to the learned societies of the time, we get the impression that Victorian steam engineers were practical and confident men possessed of firmly held views gathered from experience. Fundamental knowledge was only just being gathered in and means of experiment were limited. Steam enthusiasts of the present day show something of the same individuality and confidence. This is well exemplified in the small steamboat field by a marked preference for either a simple or a compound engine.

An absolute virtue of the compound engine is its ability to use a large ratio of expansion with a simple eccentric-driven valve gear. This can lead to a marked economy in fuel and is sufficient justification for its use when long uninterrupted passages are involved.

Other virtues sometimes attributed to the in-line compound engine really follow from the use of a multi-cranked engine. These are improved balance and uniform torque.

On land, in locomotive work particularly, the compound engine came and went. Improvements in economy were of the same kind of magnitude as could be achieved by a good compared to an indifferent driver; as was pointed out at the time, the best drivers were always allocated to the compounds. The matter was never really proven. It could be overshadowed (as with the corresponding injector or feed pump and heater controversy) by the more complex engine needing to be supported by a larger stock of spares and the longer time needed for overhaul. This could lead to a reduction in the earning power of the engine irrespective of thermal efficiency.

For river and canal boats it is really a matter of preference. The two-crank simple wins on manœuvrability and on the absence of over-expansion troubles which affect some compound engines at low power levels and speeds (*Funnel* 23-150, 27-103, 28-145). The differences in economy may be quite overshadowed by the standby losses suffered by both types when waiting for lock working.

Experiments can be misleading unless they are very carefully planned, since it is possible inadvertently to change two variables at a time. For instance, to remove the high pressure piston and to supply steam directly to the receiver means a very big change in overall ratio of expansion as well as a change from two to one cylinder working. The experiment is almost impossible to interpret. The answer is that the enthusiast should go for the method which gives him (or her) the greatest satisfaction.

The uniflow engine

The basic ideas of the uniflow engine were invented in Britain nearly one hundred years ago, but much of its development was to take place on the continent early in this century. It was just becoming popular in Britain as a mill engine in the nineteen-twenties but by then the great days of these large low-speed engines (mill engine powers were in the range 750 kW to 3000 kW – 1000 to 4000 horsepower – per cylinder) were over.

Steam enters through a valve in the cylinder head and it is exhausted through a belt of ports exposed in the cylinder walls when the piston nears the end of the stroke, hence the name uniflow (see figure 10. 2). The cut-off is generally so early in the stroke that cam-operated drop-valves are appropriate for inlet steam. The exhaust, of course, needs no valve gear. In the double acting form the piston has unusual proportions: its length is equal to the stroke less the width of the exhaust ports.

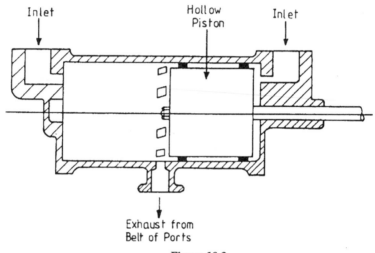

Figure 10.2

The Uniflow Engine

When the engine has an early cut-off and a clearance volume adjusted to give a compression pressure near to that of the inlet steam it has thermodynamic advantages. The economy which can be achieved in a single cylinder is better than that of a corresponding triple-expansion engine. This is achieved with much less mechanism (one cylinder and admission valve gear instead of three with both admission and exhaust valves), but that which is used has to be more refined. A large flywheel may be necessary to secure a sufficiently uniform rotation.

The clearance volume of the uniflow is critical and it is related to both the steam pressure and the condenser pressure if good results are to be obtained. Compression should be such as to reach somewhere near to the steam pressure before the inlet valve opens. This reduces irreversibility of flow with a consequent loss of available energy. Thus an engine working on a pressure of 10 bar (150 lb/in^2) and normal vacuum (0. 8 bar or 24 inches of mercury vacuum) may need a compression ratio of 40 or 50, whereas with a 6 bar

(90 lb/in^2) pressure and atmospheric exhaust, the ratio should be between 5 and 6.

The normal uniflow lacks the supreme flexibility of the simple slide-valve engine. Attempts to regulate the speed by lowering the pressure cause a negative loop in the indicator diagram. When the area of this loop approaches that of the positive, the engine comes to an abrupt halt. Control, therefore, must be by variation in cut-off rather than in pressure.

To start a large uniflow engine extra clearance volume may be opened up or an auxiliary exhaust valve may be used. In special cases such as vehicle engines a restricted exhaust may be permanently open during the compression stroke. This vents the cylinder at low speeds but because of the restriction it is less effective during times when when the speed is increased. The cycle then approaches the uniflow requirements. When the engine is double-acting the auxiliary exhaust may be built into the piston itself.

Relatively recent attempts to introduce small scale constant speed engines using modern technology sometimes used the uniflow principle. Such engines are started manually by bumping over compression, as in an internal combustion engine. The principle can be easily demonstrated by modifications to a two-stroke petrol engine. The transfer port must be blanked off and a cam-operated poppet valve arranged to admit steam through the former spark plug orifice. Engines with cast-iron pistons (rare today) particularly lend themselves to this conversion.

The "bash-valve" engine

This has become the generic term for a uniflow engine in which the inlet valve opening exactly corresponds to the piston movement for a short distance before and after top dead centre.

Such engines are reported as being in commercial production very early in the present century. They had both inlet and exhaust functions controlled by the movement of the piston over ports in the cylinder wall. Having no moving valve parts, they were exceptionally quiet and smooth running. Powers of 4 kW (5 horsepower) at 3000 rev/min are reported. In some later engines a poppet valve in the cylinder head was opened by contact with the piston when it was very near to the end of its stroke. No other valve gear was required; the exhaust was from the usual uniflow belt of ports opened in the cylinder wall when the piston approached then bottom dead centre position. It was this variant which gave the engine its popular name.

The term *bash-valve* is misleading in suggesting an element of violence in what can be a refined and elegant engine of simple construction and high thermal efficiency. The action of the engine is not necessarily violent. A piston having an approximately simple harmonic motion is moving slowly when it is very near to the end of its stroke, and the so-called bash may be manifested externally by a gentle click. For example, a 75 mm (3 inch) stroke engine working at 300 rev/min has a piston speed of only about 0.5 m/s (1. 5 ft/s) when the crank is 20° off top dead centre. The maximum valve opening would be about 2.5 mm (0.1 inch) at dead centre.

Such an engine should have a ratio of expansion approaching the ratio of steam to exhaust pressure applied to the engine.

The engine has, however, limitations. It is not self starting, indeed it needs quite powerful cranking to spin it over the first few compressions (cases of electric starters are reported). It needs a flywheel with a large moment of inertia and the engine has limited speed flexibility. It works best with a fixed steam pressure, and at low pressures the power is small for the size of the engine. It works best under a permanently coupled fixed load. The ideal load is similar to that given by a fan or blower which, increasing steeply with speed, tends to a self-regulating system. Since it must start under full steam pressure, initial acceleration is very rapid. An unloaded engine can quickly run up to destruction.

The engine has no preferred direction of rotation. Changes in steam pressure or in load can produce an abrupt reversal of rotation or can set up a state of oscillation reminiscent of the rotor of a washing machine.

CHAPTER 11

Engine Regulating and Reversing

S. Y. Gondola, Coniston Water
A lake steamer built in 1859 as a tourist facility and as a service to lakeside mansions. The long forward overhang enabled her to run stem on to the beach, whence a ladder could be used for access. In use until 1939; recently rebuilt as a National Trust project and in service again. Powered by a locomotive type boiler and a 90° Vee twin simple expansion engine.

Throttle and cut-off governing

Certain engines, such as those used on boats, rail and road locomotives and winding engines, need sensitive speed control in both directions. Others, such as electric generators, need the speed to be held constant irrespective of the load on the engine. Two methods of control are commonly available; these are *a)* throttle governing, and *b)* cut-off governing.

The former varies the steam pressure applied to the engine. The latter varies the degree of expansion. Because it is simple and cheap, the first method can be considered as normal. On marine applications the cube law of propeller power means that when the speed is reduced the propeller demand is reduced even more. To control by cut-off would be to risk over-expansion with erratic running and possibly abrupt stalling.

A combination of both methods is needed for a railway locomotive where there is no fixed relationship between power and speed. An engine used to drive an electric generator which must maintain a constant speed may exceptionally show an improvement in economy at part load if cut-off governing is used. The special properties of the uniflow engine generally require cut-off governing for anything but a very small change in load.

Reversing

A reversing gear is essential for a locomotive engine and for such duties as pit winding and rolling mills. For marine engines the subject has been considered debatable. Astern gears of the link type involve a lot of work in manufacture. Some builders of small engines have told the author that they spend more time on the link motion than on all the rest of the engine. To the Victorian engineer Thorneycroft, the need for an astern gear was not proven, even for sea-going ships. He said that the astern gear was expensive and cumbersome; although used but seldom, the parts are at work during the whole time the vessel is under way (incidentally, not true of the slip eccentric gear). Seamen have departed from the old sailing-ship days; it is an indulgence to the weakness of the modern mariner that the sternway screw has been devised.

Thorneycroft did not get much support in the commercial field, but many affluent yachtsmen despised power of any kind, either ahead or astern. Some do so today, even with quite large vessels.

On moderate sized launches, up to say 6m in length, an oar or a boathook can often do all that is required, but much depends on the waters where the vessel is to be used. On a river such as the Thames where one is surrounded by much bigger vessels, some with possibly aggressive drivers, or nearly as bad, by rowing boats whose hirers are new to the waters, the astern gear can be considered essential. On a secluded pond or quiet river (if any such there be) it is not necessary and the engine is certainly easier to make and may be quieter without it. On some navigations an astern drive is a condition for the granting of a licence.

Port changing

The simplest means of reversing, that of interchanging inlet and exhaust passages, occurs in the rather uneconomical engine where the valve has neither lap nor lead. This has been used where simplicity of construction and instant response are more important than economical running. These engines have had many applications on shipboard, particularly for steering engines and for lifeboat and anchor winches (figure 11.1).

The slip eccentric

The reversing of a slide valve engine with outside admission involves moving the centre of the eccentric sheave from position A (figure 11.2) to the mirror position A'. This is easily done if the sheave is free to rotate on the crankshaft between appropriate stops. The slip eccentric was used in the early days of railways and it still has some application for small boat engines. Commonly,

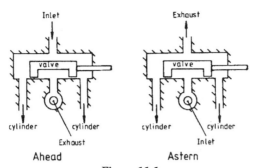

Figure 11.1

Port Changing Reversing

the eccentric is moved relative to the shaft by a helix which rotates with the shaft but is free to slide along it. *Gondola* is fitted with a reversing gear of this type.

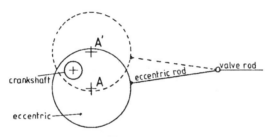

Figure 11.2

Slip Eccentric Reversing

Link valve motions

A more convenient method of reversal is to use two fixed eccentric sheaves with their centres fixed at *A* and *A'* respectively (figure 11.3). Movement of the link enables either of the eccentrics to operate the valve rods. The other simply oscillates the link without moving the valve. In due course it was found that intermediate positions of the link could be used to control the power of the engine as an alternative to throttling. Examination of the mechanism shows that movement of the link from the extremity towards the centre corresponds (approximately) to an equivalent eccentric of reduced travel and increased angle of advance. The Stephenson and other linkworks soon became popular on the railways. The Stephenson remained normal for industrial locomotives and for marine work so long as such engines were built.

Two other important link motions were the Gooch and the Allen. In the Stephenson the link is moved relative to the valve rod. In the Gooch, the valve rod is moved relative to the link. In the Allen both valve rod and link are moved in opposite directions. This enables the control system in a horizontal engine to be balanced as regards vertical forces; it is thus easier to operate. The author associates it with heavy rolling mill engines which were reversed at each pass of the ingot.

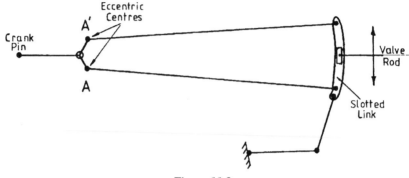

Figure 11.3
Link Reversing Gear

Linking up

Reduced travel and increased angle of advance tend to keep the lead the same (more or less) and to bring the points of cut-off, release and compression earlier in the cycle. The ratio of expansion is increased while at the same time the steam consumption is reduced. This means of control can tend toward a higher efficiency than does throttling of the steam supply. It is much used for locomotive work. When a heavy train is starting up, cut-off is late as the powerful chimney blasts indicate. As the load eases off cut-off can become earlier and the engine can work more quietly using less steam. Finally, when running at high speed down a long bank, an even earlier cut-off with adequate compression enables steam economy to be maintained.

A large range of cut-off control is neither desired nor appropriate in marine engines where, when a high speed is called for, a much higher power is always involved. Even so, on large multi-cylinder engines a small degree of independent link adjustment was often provided on each cylinder for power balancing.

Radial valve gears

The desirable requirement for reversing and regulating an engine is that the valve should have a constant lead as the eccentric centre is moved from *A* to *A'* (figure 11.2). In other words, when the engine is at rest and set at dead centre it should be possible to move the valve gear all the way from *A* to *A'* without any movement being imparted to the valve. Hence the term *radial valve gear* for a linkwork which satisfies this requirement. The Stephenson link is not able to do this and in consequence can produce a negative loop on the indicator diagram when it is very near to mid-gear.

The basic requirement for a radial gear capable of reversing is that the valve should should have two components of motion, *a* and *b*.

a is a component fixed in amount at an angle of 180° (or 0°, depending on inside or outside admission). This is the lead component.

b is a component at 90° on either side of the crank, adjustable from *A* to *A*'. This is the valve opening component. However complex a motion may seem to be, when examined it can be seen to aim at these requirements.

The Hackworth was the parent of all radial valve gears (fig 11. 4). This uses a single eccentric set at 180° (or 0°) to the crank.

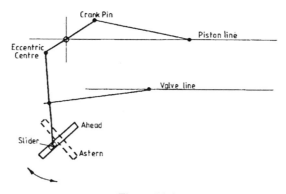

Figure 11.4
The Hackworth Valve Gear

The eccentric rod terminates in a block which works along a slide. When the slide points toward the centre of the crankshaft, only a 180° or 0° lead component of motion can influence the valve rod. When the slide is inclined, a 90° or valve opening component is superimposed on the valve rod. The steeper the inclination of the slide, the greater is the opening. Inclination of the slide in the opposite sense corresponds to a reversed rotation of the engine.

The Marshall and Bremme gears are very closely related to the Hackworth.

Not quite so closely related but of the same family are linkworks such as the Joy which are able to do without an eccentric. A point on the connecting rod oscillates a linkwork so designed that it has a point which moves in a closed curve approximating to a circle. This nearly circular motion is used as is the eccentric of a Hackworth gear.

Gears such as Walshaert's pick up the two components of valve motion from separate parts of the engine in a manner which is self-evident from inspection of an outside cylinder locomotive (figure 11.5). The fixed (180° or 0°) component comes from the cross head. The 90° component comes from a return crank or from an eccentric. Variation of this, both in magnitude and direction, is achieved by use of an expansion link. A variation of this gear employed by Kitson for tramway locomotives used a point on the coupling rod instead of a return crank.

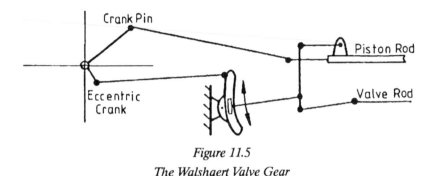

Figure 11.5
The Walshaert Valve Gear

Of the very large number of valve gears which have been used or proposed, the Stephenson and the Walshaert have most stood the test of time. However, Hackworth, Marshall and Joy gears can occasionally be seen in use.

Valve diagrams

Any significant adjustment to the simple steam engine may involve the valve events. There is apparently a formidable list of inter-dependent variables involved in even a trivial change. These can be lap and lead and valve opening, both for steam and for exhaust. Also there are piston positions corresponding to points of admission, cut-off, release and compression. These variables are cumbersome to handle analytically. This was realised early in the steam story. In the 1850s graphical constructions were devised which illustrated them in a simple way.

One construction, that of Reuleaux, is here described without proof. As an illustrative example, it is simplified by assuming that the connecting rod is fairly long compared with the radius of the crank. A step-by-step method of construction is given (figure 11.6).

(1)   Draw a circle, centre O, whose radius represents on some scale the throw of the eccentric. The diameter then represents the valve travel. (To another, quite different, scale the circle can also represent the movement of the crank and piston since both go round at the same speed.)

(2)   With centre O draw another circle whose radius represents the steam lap. With centre at A on the horizontal diameter of the large circle, draw another circle whose radius represents the lead to steam.

(3)   Draw a line tangential to both lap and lead circles, below the lead circle for positive lead, above it for negative.

(4)   Draw a line through O perpendicular to the tangent line. The angle θ between this line and the vertical OC is the angle of advance.

(5)   For any angular crank position measured from AO the corresponding valve position can be measured on the appropriate scale by the projection of the point onto KL.

(6)   The corresponding piston position can be measured by the projection of the point onto AB (again using the appropriate scale). Thus G represents the point of cut-off when AB represents the piston stroke (the point A representing top dead centre).

(7)   Exhaust or inside lap is rarely used, but can be illustrated in the same way. If it is, as is usual, zero, then a line can be drawn through O parallel to the tangent line. This intersects the main circle at H, the point of release, and J, the point of compression.

(8)   The four points of the diagram – admission A, cut-off G, release H and compression J – can be defined along the piston stroke base AOB and projected downwards to draw a hypothetical indicator diagram.

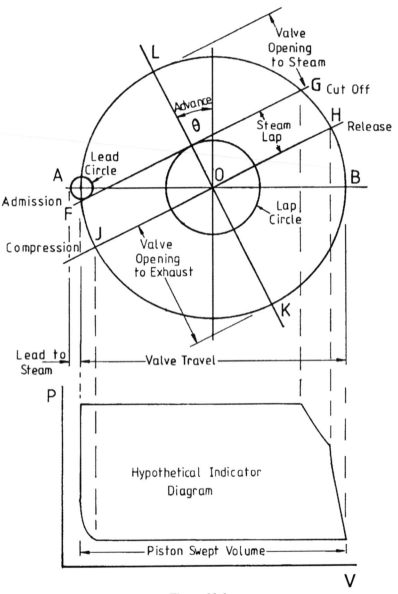

Figure 11.6
The Reuleaux Valve Diagram

CHAPTER 12

On Balancing

*Leeds
and
Liverpool
Canal
steam
boats*
Some of these
were in service
in the early
1950s. They
had 90° Vee
compound
engines.

General

The balancing of engines, that is the avoidance of cyclical forces originating with acceleration of moving parts and transmitted through the bearings to the foundations, was not taken very seriously in the early days of steam. Even though machine parts were extremely heavy, speeds were low and land engines were generally secured to masonry foundations. The situation at sea was not much different. Indeed, one almost wonders if vibrating shudders passing through the hull gave the mariners a sense of assurance that all was well in the engine department. One hundred years earlier, Watt had written of his first (mal-adjusted) engine in Cornwall, 'The velocity, violence, magnitude and horrible noise of the engine give universal satisfaction.'

As with many other advances in reciprocating steam engines, the pace of development was forced by the locomotive. Two horizontal cylinders impart a swaying motion. This can be eliminated by rotating balance weights. Unfortunately, in doing so new vertical forces are introduced. These can introduce a rail-damaging hammer blow. The first lesson, therefore, is that a reciprocating force cannot be eliminated by a rotating one, but its direction can be changed. Locomotive balancing remained a problem and a subject for research as long as railway steam existed.

Locomotive and marine balancing are further complicated by the desire to avoid the dead-centre position from which an engine cannot be started without external assistance.

With one exception (the 90° Vee arrangement) a steam engine designer needs four lines of cylinders to achieve both balance and self-starting. This is one of the reasons why the four-cylinder triple-expansion in-line engine was once so popular (but how we used to despise anyone who confused a four-cylinder-triple with a quadruple-expansion engine!)

Rotating disturbances can arise from lack of homogeneity in a casting, or they may be inherent in the mechanical design, for example a crank and its pin. This kind of disturbance can normally be dealt with.

Reciprocating disturbances arise from such parts as the piston, the piston rod and the crosshead as they are accelerated first in one direction and then in the other. The associated forces are transmitted ultimately through the bearings to the foundation. In general a reciprocating force can only be balanced by another reciprocating force.

Balancing of rotating masses

Static balance

If a wheel is supported on a shaft which in turn rests on two horizontal rails, generally tapered towards the top and in workshop usage referred to as knife edges (figure 12.1), then even though it has been truly machined it may tend to roll until one particular point on the wheel always comes to the lowest position.

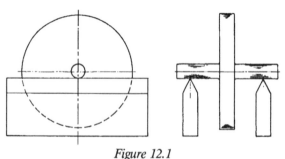

Figure 12.1
Static Out-of-Balance

Hence there is an out-of-balance force, due in this case to the material not being quite homogeneous. If such a wheel is rotated an out-of-balance force is transmitted to the bearings. The severity of such a force depends on the degree of out-of-balance and on the speed of the wheel. Out-of-balance forces are undesirable and in some cases they can be eliminated by lightening the heavy side of the wheel. The holes left when small amounts of metal have been removed by drilling can often be seen on automobile flywheel rims. The magnitude of the force due to an out-of-balance mass is proportional to the mass and to the square of the rotational speed. When such a wheel has been balanced statically it should remain in balance when it is in motion.

Dynamic balance – pitching moments

Let us now consider two wheels (1) and (2) on one axle (figure 12.2) where one wheel is out-of-balance by the equivalent of a mass M at radius r. This could be balanced so far as the knife edge test is concerned by a similar mass on the opposite side of the other wheel, or by lightening the other wheel on the same side. However, this system would not be balanced when it was rotated. The axial distance between the two out-of-balance forces which now exist would create a pitching (and yawing) moment.

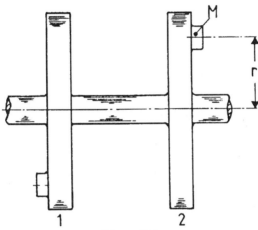

Figure 12.2
Dynamic Out-of-Balance

A two-cylinder engine with cranks at 180° or a three cylinder engine with cranks at 120° can be in static balance, but still be unbalanced dynamically. Such a system can only be balanced by adding or removing mass at two separate axial positions. Dynamic balancing machines, which measure the forces on the bearings as the shaft rotates, can be used to find the masses required.

Forces originating in the engine connecting rod

The connecting rod is a troublesome piece of ironmongery. Part of the big end may be considered as having rotary motion, most of the small end as having reciprocating motion. Some designers would find the mass of the rod and add half to the rotating system and half to the reciprocating system. Others consider it more refined to support the rod horizontally (figure 12.3) and divide its mass in the ratio of the reaction forces at each end. Either method involves compromise and guesswork. Attempts at complete analysis lead to complications which are rarely justifiable.

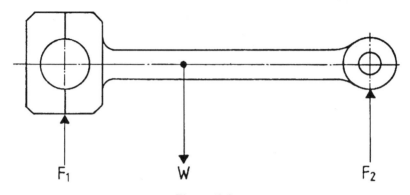

Figure 12.3
Balancing of Connecting Rod

The connecting rod also produces a quite separate source of vibrations. For compactness most connecting rods are of only moderate length if measured in terms of piston stroke. This means that, given a uniform angular velocity of the crank shaft, the motion of the piston is more complicated than the simple harmonic which every engineer desires. Mathematicians have shown that a vibratory motion, not of the simple harmonic type, can be represented as a fundamental simple harmonic motion on which are superimposed other harmonic motions at multiple frequencies. The double frequency motion is often prominent in reciprocating engines. The forces corresponding to the fundamental are referred to as primary and those at double speed as the secondary. Formerly, high-class motor car engines might incorporate special mechanisms to balance the double frequency disturbances, or they might resort to six-cylinder engines which can be designed to eliminate them internally. Nowadays, lighter reciprocating parts and rubber suspensions are used to make four-cylinder engines more acceptable. The author has not met harmonic balancing systems in a steam engine context, but they are not uncommon in high-grade diesels.

Reciprocating balance of the 90° Vee engine

Experience suggests that forces due to a reciprocating mass can only be balanced by those of another reciprocating mass, but there is an exception. Mathematics can show that the resultant force of two reciprocating masses acting at right angles (figure 12.4a) is the same as that of a single out-of-balance rotating mass (figure 12.4b). Accordingly, if the 90° Vee twin engine (with the cylinders in the same plane) and a rotating balance weight are suitably combined, a system in complete primary balance can result. Furthermore, if such an engine is double-acting, it can start from any crank position. A further virtue of the 90° Vee engine is that it cannot introduce a pitching moment, since its residual secondary forces are all in the same plane. The search for near-perfection in engine design can begin with the 90° Vee configuration.

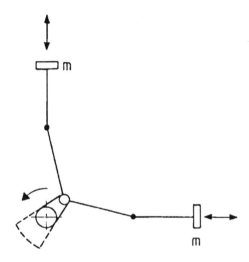

Figure 12.4a
Two Out-of-Balance forces at right angles

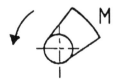

Figure 12.4b
Out-of-Balance Rotating Mass

CHAPTER 13

Application of Steam to Small Inland Craft

Steam Dinghy

A modern G.R.P. dinghy 3.6 m (12 ft) long, converted to steam. Sketched on a visit to Loch Lomond.

There is a joy and a peace beside still waters which has been sought after by civilised people in the many cultures in the world which have been sufficiently affluent to give them the time to contemplate. One can think of the Twenty-third Psalm, or of Far Eastern pictures which show water gardens, and of the place of river backwaters in old universities. In our own time there is an urge to seek the peace of rivers, lakes and canals. Often also the very means used destroys the peace which is so urgently sought after. A small steam (or maybe electric) boat is perhaps the least intrusive after a manually propelled one.

Stability

After an ability to float, an assurance that the craft will float the right way up is desirable. This leads to the study of stability.

The centre of gravity of the water displaced by the boat is called the centre of buoyancy. By definition this must be below the water-line (denoted by the point B in figure 13.1a). The centre of gravity of the hull and machinery, particularly if there is a vertical boiler, is likely to be above the water-line (point G).

If the boat is now heeled over (figure 13.1b), the shape of the displaced section changes and B moves to B'. There is now a buoyancy upthrust through B' and a weight acting through G. If G is below the point M, the two forces acting together exert a righting moment and the boat should heave itself upright. If G is above M, then the forces tend to increase the displacement, possibly to the point of overturning.

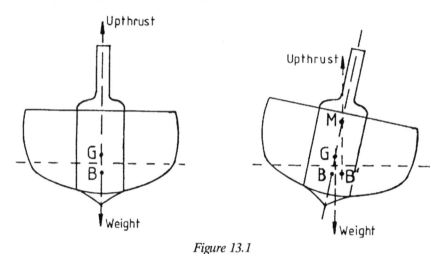

Figure 13.1

a) Forces on Upright boat　　　　　　　*b) Forces on Heeled Boat*

M is called the *metacentre* and the distance MG (denoted by m) is called the *metacentric height*. If the metacentric height is positive, the boat is stable.

The metacentric height is not constant with angle of heel. Generally a ship is designed to have a fairly small initial value of m when she is nearly vertical, and for m to increase fairly rapidly as the inclination increases. The value can be calculated, and is normally checked experimentally by the process known as inclining. Weights are transferred from one side of the ship to the other and the change of inclination is measured. This is done as a safety test on sea-going ships and it is one of the many factors which enter into the international handicapping system for off-shore sailing yachts.

Undue water in the bilge is potentially dangerous. If a boat heels, the bilge water surges to the lowest point and tends to increase the heeling. Capsizing is by no means a remote academic point. Apart from the history of mediaeval warships which overturned (*Vasa, Mary Rose,* etc.), cases of capsizing still occur due to wrong design, change of loading or shifting cargo moving the ship's centre of gravity. On a small scale, the author has known of a home-built canal boat (whose owner insisted on having standing headroom) capsizing soon after launching. Lake launches, which often have fairly lofty cabins, have been known to capsize and sink on their moorings due to unexpected heavy falls of snow.

Resistance in calm water

The power available, and indeed the power requirement, for a small steam launch is quite small and the weight of the plant may be relatively great. To achieve desired results, then, there should be a deliberate pursuit of excellence at every stage of the design.

This must begin with the boat. It is well established that a displacement boat has two, largely independent, components of resistance. First is the skin friction of the hull. This depends on the surface finish and the wetted area. It is significantly influenced by quite small unevennesses or by organic slime. Sailing yacht owners will go to extreme lengths to make sure that their boat's underwater surface is as smooth and clean as it can be. The second component is wave-making. Water pushed aside at the bow initially piles up and then starts at least two systems of waves. Diverging waves move away in a chevron formation and carry energy which is irrecoverable. They also start a series of transverse waves. The void left at the stern also starts its own set of waves.

Transverse waves are of the type where the crest to crest length is related to the speed of the boat. The greater the speed the longer the wave. As the speed of the boat increases the bow train of waves can influence the stern train, sometimes reinforcing them, sometimes cancelling them out, so that the characteristic resistance curve has a series of humps and hollows. However, there is a limit to this process when the length of the bow wave is comparable to the length of the boat. From the shape of the resistance curve, this is known as *the last hump*. The significance is that the boat squats by the stern and in effect is always trying to go uphill. Increase of engine power now signifies little as regards increase in speed. A boat which settles comfortably at five knots may need double the power if it is to reach six knots.

"The critical speed"

This limiting speed is called the critical speed. There are now a hundred years of consistent experience that for a boat of good shape the critical speed is related to the square root of the length. A well-known formula gives the critical speed in knots related to the length in feet as

$$v = k\sqrt{(L)}$$

where the constant k normally lies within the range 1.1 to 1.4. (Other values of k can be calculated for use with metric units; there is also a version of the formula which is independent of the system of units used.) k is called, rather imprecisely, the speed/length ratio. Higher speeds (i.e. higher values of k) are possible, but with a round bilge boat it is rarely worth attempting to reach them. The length L is an 'effective wave-making length' which can, as a first approximation, be taken as the waterline length. Determination of the effective length is one of the objects of the very complex measurements to which racing yachts are subjected.

Measured kilometre tests during the Steam Boat Association's annual Windermere regatta suggest that the traditional launch form is likely to have a speed/length ratio of about 1.25. Higher figures have been observed – up to 1.7 in the author's experience.

There is no need to try to work a boat up to its critical speed. Few merchant ships, even those on express routes, can afford to do so. Length sufficient to be able to achieve the desired speed with the available power is useful but excess length, particularly if associated with a narrow beam, can be detrimental.

From the author's experience, a speed/length ratio of about 1 can give a pleasing and adequate still water performance and one that is not likely to be inconsiderate to other water users. Figure 13.2 shows the speeds corresponding to several speed/length ratios for a range of small boat sizes.

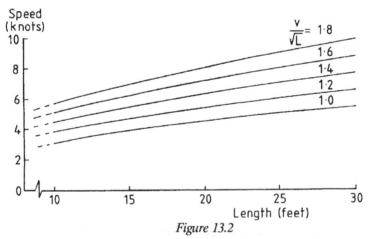

Figure 13.2

Boat Speed and Length for different Speed/Length Ratios

About a hundred years ago it became fashionable for both sailing and steam pleasure boats built in the United Kingdom to be so long and narrow as to be referred to at the time as 'planks on edge'. This tendency was made worse when it became built into a code of measurement. These mistakes in design were not made in the United States, and there was no doubt at all about the excellence of their boats.

The last twenty years have seen intense competitive effort put into tank testing research on yacht hull design. Shorter and beamier types with less depth of hull have emerged as forms of low resistance. These forms have enhanced initial stability and because of reduced wetted area and superb surface finish their low speed resistance is very small indeed. Length to beam ratios of 3:1 can be compared with 8:1 for vessels of 80 years ago.

When applied to a sailing yacht these forms need a deep fin and skeg to give lateral resistance. As applied to a steam launch the only skeg needed may be one to protect the propeller. The excellence of one sailing vessel form as the basis for a low-powered steam launch (speed/length ratio about 1) is supported by personal experience.

Propulsion

The fundamental requirement is for a large thrust area and for a low velocity of the propelled stream. A 0.36 m (14 in) diameter propeller can be twice as effective as one of 0.25 m (10 in) diameter which absorbs the same amount of power. Also desirable is a low rotational speed to reduce friction losses. This is generally met on steam launches by using a propeller whose pitch is greater than its diameter, and of course by a high polish on the propeller surface. The appropriate speed is often a few hundred rev/min, which is well suited to a steam engine, but outside the range of the modern internal combustion engine without a reduction gearbox.

Paddle wheels

The paddle wheel was an early occurrence in the steam boat story, but it did not appear very significantly for pleasure launches in this country. It is easy for a paddle to have a very large thrust area; hence at low speeds it can be quiet and efficient. It is well adapted to shallow, weedy water. However, if speeds are increased it is not so good because of the surface disturbance it creates, and has obvious limitations in a seaway. The simple radial blade can produce a thump each time a blade (generally called a float) hits the water. This is not generally a distressing noise but it does impose a shock load on the machinery. The use of a feathering paddle, with linkwork to adjust the angle of the blade so that it enters and leaves the water without shock, can alleviate the problem. Such systems were used on the fast cross-channel steamers developed in the early part of this century for services such as the English Channel, the Irish Sea and the Clyde.

Sternwheels

The stern paddle wheel has much to commend it. It can accelerate and so neutralize the wake which is being dragged after the boat. In the event of grounding in soft mud, astern operation can wash mud away from under the hull. However, it has a structural problem following from the overhung weight astern. This was formerly balanced by putting the boiler near the bow. Thus a shallow hull was subject to bending moment. Commonly a lattice girder structure was used to stiffen the hull. The upper boom of the girder could act as a base for an upper deck. On a very small scale the length of a sternwheeler almost precludes its use as a trailer boat.

Sternwheel steam launches are much more popular in North America than in the United Kingdom. One of the problems is the construction of a special, rather large, low-speed steam engine. Some owners opt for a geared drive from a faster running engine; either method can be satisfactory. The author operated a 6 m (20 ft) stern wheel boat (alas, not steam powered) for many years. This used a paddle 1.5 m (5 ft) long by 1.25 m (4 ft) diameter with six floats each 0.2 m (8 in) deep. Probably a rather larger wheel with more floats might have been better and worked with less shock. A centre-geared drive to twin wheels using an automobile differential box can work satisfactorily. Outboard bearings on the paddle shaft can be made of wood, with generous clearances, and work well lubricated by water dripping off the floats.

Speed measurement

The performance of a boat/propulsion system combination (and in particular the change in performance arising out of some change in the set-up) can only be determined by accurate measurement of speed through the water. One method is to measure the time taken over a measured mile or kilometre marked by transit points at both ends. It is best to use an observer in the boat, since otherwise two observers in close communication are needed. Runs should be made in both directions, as close together in time as possible, and in minimum wind and current conditions. Averaging the ground speeds (not the times) will to some extent balance out the effects of small amounts of wind and current. If the two times are very different, the trial should be repeated when conditions improve.

Commercially available boat speedometers are useful for finding the effects of changes, but since they are dependent on the localised flow round the boat, they should not be relied upon for absolute speed measurement unless they have been recently calibrated under closely similar conditions.

General

Despite increasing analytic and experimental knowledge of the many variables involved in the matching of hull, engine, propeller and speed, matters pertaining to boats still retain an element of 'art and mystery'. This is what makes them so interesting. Access to accumulated experience is the most valuable of all guidance. One can study the (mostly successful) boats listed in *Steam Boats of the British Isles* (and its predecessor the *Steam Boat Index*) and the *North American Steam Boat Register*. Also *Funnel* continually adds to the sum of recorded experience.

CHAPTER 14

Engine Testing and Characteristics

Watt Engine

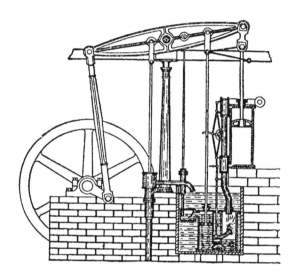

James Watt made a number of significant improvements to the steam engine, notably the introduction of a separate condenser, the use of higher pressure steam and numerous innovations in valve gear and linkwork. The diagram shows a double-acting, spray-condensing engine of 1784.

Systematic testing

The testing of a power plant was once a normal activity for a mechanical engineer, but it is rarely practised today. Hence a few points derived from personal experience may be worth recording.

The absolute principle which should always be in the experimenter's mind is not to vary too many things at the same time – preferably only one. This greatly simplifies the problem of determining cause and effect.

Instrumentation

Measurements which can be made directly in terms of mass, length and time are always desirable. Standards of these are widely available and indeed they could be improvised almost anywhere, subsequently to be referred to standard quantities. Simple measurements are desirable. A bucket and a spring balance may well be preferable to a flow-meter in the measurement of condensate. Pressure measurements are more difficult, since most pressure gauges are inferential. If the pressure is small, a gauge can be calibrated against a fluid column. Higher pressures are calibrated against a loaded ram pressing on a fluid, but such gauge testing facilities are rare outside laboratories. For temperature measurements, one is almost bound to rely on the mercury in glass thermometer.

The basic measurement of speed is achieved by counting the number of revolutions in a given time. For engines of moderate speed, small hand-held reduction gear instruments which could be held against the centre hole in the end of a shaft were formerly available in toolshops. Tachometers, which are inferential, are useful once they have been calibrated. A simple instrument may be made with a small permanent magnet dynamo (or motor being driven as a dynamo). The terminal voltage, when only a minute current is drawn, is proportional to speed. Thus a voltmeter (which can of course be remote from the moving machinery) can be calibrated in terms of speed.

Torque and Power

A convenient method of measuring torque is an absorption dynamometer in which all the power produced by the engine is absorbed by friction on a brake. This is the origin of the term *brake horsepower*. *Shaft power* is a better usage since there are other methods of measuring the torque.

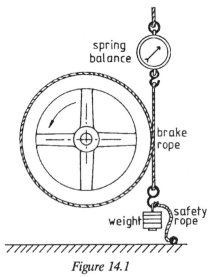

Figure 14.1

Rope Brake Dynamometer

A small engine in a teaching laboratory was normally fitted with a rope brake. The brake wheel could be integral with the flywheel, and it was water cooled. The brake rope normally passed once around the wheel. It was loaded by a weight at the bottom and attached to a spring balance at the top. The difference of tension above and below the brake wheel multiplied by its effective radius gave the torque. Power is then torque multiplied by angular velocity (figure 14.1).

The danger inherent in such brakes is that of jamming, which could throw the weight around the wheel. Likelihood of jamming is reduced if the brake wheel has a wide, flat surface between flanges, and if a well-oiled natural fibre rope is used. A very secure stop which prevents the weight from being lifted more than a few centimetres (an inch or so) should always be used.

The mass M at the bottom will exert a force Mg under gravity. Spring balances measure force, but most are calibrated in terms of mass. This conflict between the laboratory and the market place seems impossible to avoid, but the reading of mass can be accepted because g, the acceleration due to gravity, varies but little from place to place. If the spring balance reading is m, then the difference in tension between the ends is

$(M - m)g$

The effective radius of the brake wheel can be taken as its actual radius, R, plus the radius of the rope, r. The torque is thus

$(M - m)g(R + r)$

and the power, which is torque times angular velocity, is

$2 \pi N (M - m)g(R + r)$

where N is the rotational speed in revolutions per second. If R and r are in metres and M and m in kilogrammes, then the appropriate value of g is 9.81 m/s^2 and the power will be in watts. In traditional units, the masses are in pounds and the radii in feet. g is 32.2 ft/s^2 and the power is in foot-poundals per second. This may be converted to Horsepower by dividing by 17,710.

A very valuable kind of brake, but one likely to be available only in a specialist laboratory, is the hydraulic brake originally invented by W. Froude in 1877 for use on full-scale ships. Its principle of operation is similar to a pump; the energy of the shaft is transferred to water which is then brought to rest. The torque necessary to restrain the brake is measured with weights or a spring balance on a lever arm. The *fluid flywheel* of automobile application can be taken as having developed from this brake. Its advantages are that it does not snatch and is very stable.

Torque can also be measured in transmission without wasting the power. One method is to use the twist or winding up of a shaft while it is running (the twist is usually extremely small). This can be done optically, using a stroboscope, or with strain gauges and slip-rings. This method has marine applications.

A completely mechanical method uses the elements of a bevel-type differential gear; in doing so, however, it reverses the direction of rotation. This device may be improvised from parts of a discarded automotive differential. The engine is connected to one wheel shaft and the load to the other. The propeller shaft coupling is locked to the housing. The torque required to restrain the housing is twice the torque being transmitted through the system.

This is one variant of a more general system. Any gear box which changes the speed will change the torque in inverse proportion (assuming friction in the gearbox is negligible). The ratio of the input and output torques is the reciprocal of the speed ratio. The difference between the input and output torques is the torque needed to restrain the gearbox. From these two relationships, the two torques are readily calculated.

Testing procedure

A heat engine needs to run for a reasonable time to ensure that thermal conditions have settled down before the readings can be considered reliable. The time, of course, depends on the engine concerned. In small plants, half an hour may be sufficient.

All readings should be recorded as taken. Known corrections can be applied later. There is then no uncertainty if someone else has to work out the results. Principal readings should be recorded on a graph as the test proceeds. Errors can thus be spotted early. Finally, all the readings should be recorded on a single sheet of paper or on successive pages of a notebook.

Power/speed characteristics

Prime mover characteristics when speed is variable are so interesting and illuminating that it is worth first looking at those for quite different types of machine. From these we may see how a steam reciprocator fits into a general pattern (figure 14.2).

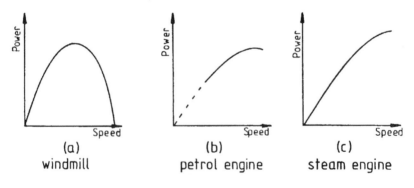

Figure 14.2

Power/Speed Characteristics of Prime Movers

Curve (a) is the characteristic of a low-speed multi-bladed windmill subject to a constant wind in a laboratory. This is one of the few devices where the process can be observed all the way from rest to "runaway". The power/speed curve starts from zero – where there is torque but no speed. At the fast end it falls towards zero – there is speed but no torque. In between there is both speed and torque. At one speed maximum power is obtained. The ideal working point is just a little faster than this, on the falling part of the characteristic.

Curve (b) is a motor car type of petrol engine. It contrasts markedly with (a). At low speed it will not run at all. At fixed throttle it may not be capable of stable running until the speed is about 1500 rev/min. Thereafter the curve climbs steadily to a peak and then begins to fall due to the restriction of flow through the carburettor and inflow passages. It is not generally prudent to run this type of engine much above peak power. Since the useful speed range is so limited, this type of engine needs a clutch and gearbox for its normal duties.

A multi-cylinder steam engine has a power curve (c) which starts from zero speed, where the torque is maximum. This is what makes it so effective as a railway or road locomotive – it requires no clutch or gears. How far it can rise up the power curve depends on its construction. Since traditional construction is at best only partially balanced, the experimenter must be prudent as to how high a speed the engine is allowed to reach. Very high speed steam engines can, of course, be made, but their construction is likely to resemble closely that of the modern internal combustion engine.

Any engine which works on the rising part of its characteristic is inherently unstable since speed and power increase together. That is why a factory engine needs a governor. A vehicle engine is under constant control by its driver. Very small petrol engines, used for battery charging, have been made which work on the falling part of their characteristic. They thus require no throttle control or governor, but they are of low power and very unusual. A marine engine is governed by the nature of the propeller power demand, which has a power absorption characteristic which increases more rapidly than that of the engine.

The characteristics of a steam engine

One of the first characteristics to be studied intensively was the relation between power and steam consumption when the speed was held constant. This arose about a hundred years ago when steam engines were first being used for central station electrical supply. A feature of the electrical load, then as now, was the marked changes in load which could occur over a relatively short time. Since the electrical voltage had to be held constant, the speed had also to be held constant no matter what the power demand might be. Economy at very light load became important; the machine had to be kept running even though its earnings were negligible.

The tests were undertaken by that pioneer of the high-speed steam engine, P.W. Willans. The results were remarkable and they had such an effect on power station technology that the term *Willans' Line* is used today when referring to the performance of the largest of steam turbines. It refers to the graph connecting shaft output power with steam consumption.

Willans' line

Willans' line is the relation between steam consumption and the power developed when a steam engine is run at constant speed and has the steam supply pressure controlled by a throttle valve.

Test procedure

(1)   Run the engine at the required speed on no load. When thermal conditions have settled down, measure the steam consumption (for example, by collecting the condensate and weighing it). This gives the first point on the graph (figure 14.3).

(2)   Increase the load in increments of about 20% of the anticipated full load. Proceed until the whole of the steam consumption rate/power curve can be plotted.

From past experience, it is probable that the plotted points will lie close to a straight line. This is Willans' line, and the fact that it is straight has even been dignified by the title of *Willans' Law*. Of course, it is not a law of nature, but over the last hundred years many thousands of such graphs are consistent with a linear relationship. Indeed, tests suggesting other forms of curve are suspect and should be examined critically.

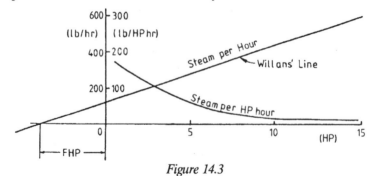

Figure 14.3

Steam Consumption/Power Characteristic – Willans' Line

All experimental points are subject to error. If a line can be drawn smoothly through them, then it probably evens out the errors and is nearer to the truth than are the points themselves. Hence derived values, such as steam consumption per horsepower-hour and mechanical efficiency are better taken from the smooth line than from the original points.

The probability of Willans' line being straight is such that two sets of readings of power and steam consumption, one at low load and one at full load, can be used with a reasonable degree of confidence to predict performance at loads in between them.

Deductions from Willans' line

By re-plotting the same data with each point divided by the power, we can obtain a curve showing the consumption of steam per horsepower-hour. This is a direct measure of the efficiency of the engine. The curve illustrated (which is based on a test carried out by the author nearly 50 years ago) shows how very inefficient an engine becomes when run at part load but normal speed. In this case, the unit cost of power was quadrupled when the engine ran at 20% of full load.

Since the tendency to follow Willans' line is by no means limited to steam engines but applies closely to many internal combustion engines as well, it is generally uneconomical to use any large engine running fast to generate a small power.

If the Willans line is extended backward until it cuts the line of zero steam consumption, a negative reading of power may be obtained. This is an indication of the amount of power required to drive the engine alone, before any power is taken from the shaft. It is mainly due to friction in the engine.

The simulation of a propeller load

In contrast to the constant speed load imposed by an electrical generator, a marine propeller imposes a load which is markedly dependent on the speed of rotation. Basically, the load varies as the cube of the speed of rotation. Superimposed on this is the engine bearing and gland friction, whose power demands are fairly closely proportional to the speed of rotation. We assume that the propeller demand is known, and we wish to know the extent to which a particular engine can meet it. The propeller demand will be a curve whose form is sketched in figure 14.4. Unless a special hydraulic dynamometer is available, a series of engine tests in which the speed is varied and the power measured (at a number of constant steam supply pressures) is necessary.

Figure 14.4

Matching of Engine and Propeller Characteristics

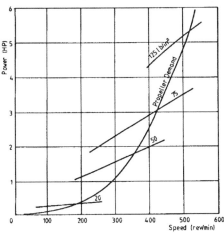

For any one steam pressure, the torque of the engine will be fairly constant, but will tend to drop at higher speeds as fluid friction plays a bigger role. If the engine could stand it, the power curve would reach a peak and then begin to fall. The series of characteristic power/speed curves at constant steam pressure can be superimposed on the propeller power demand curve. The points of intersection show the required steam pressure for any desired propeller operating point. Knowing the engine power, speed and steam pressure, steam consumption and other variables can then be more intensively studied. The curves shown on figure 14.4 are for a 5 HP 400 rev/min engine.

Engine governing

Some engines are constantly under manual control, such as those which drive cranes, hoists and land vehicles. These meet constantly varying demands which are regulated by the engine driver. Others, such as marine engines, have a control imposed by the nature of the load. As speed increases the power demand of the propeller increases at a much faster rate than does the power delivered by the engine. Overriding manual control is used only for low speeds and in emergency, for example to prevent engine racing when pitching is severe.

Engines driving industrial or electrical loads which need to run at constant speed, however, need automatic control of speed in response to change of load. The speed change signal generally derives from centrifugal effects such as the well-known governor balls. Alternatively, on an electrical generator the signal may be derived from the voltage generated by the dynamo.

The signal may be applied (with or without servo assistance) either via a throttle valve or, less commonly, to cause a variation in the point of cut-off. The throttle governing gives Willans' linear relationship between steam consumption and power. Cut-off governing has a different effect. Up to a point it may lead to greater economy since it avoids the irreversibility of the throttle valve; take too far it leads to over-expansion and loss of economy.

If a similar test to that of Willans is carried out on an engine governed by cut-off, the lines are somewhat modified, often becoming concave. The resulting specific steam consumption now has a minimum. At low power the negative loop due to over- expansion is dominant. The high ratio of expansion now increases the specific consumption of steam and leads to a falling economy.

CHAPTER 15

Concerning Entropy

Maxwell's Demon

James Clerk Maxwell (1831-1879) proposed a demon who could distinguish between fast and slow molecules of a gas, thus dividing it up into hot and cold portions. This reduces the entropy of the gas, and contravenes the Second Law of Thermodynamics. The demon cannot therefore exist. This sketch is therefore pure imagination.

General

Thermal studies which are to get further than the very practical aspects mentioned in this book are helped by a quantity called *entropy*. This is only one of several mathematical concepts which are used to obtain deeper understanding. These notes are meant to give the merest introduction to ways in which further studies may be directed.

Entropy is one of the few quantities which tell us which way a reaction can proceed. It is one of the consequences of the Second Law of Thermodynamics that the entropy of a closed system (whose definition need not concern us here) can never get less. We can burn a fuel in air to make exhaust gases, ash, etc. and liberate heat. But heating up a mixture of ash and gases will never generate coal and air. The basic fuel has a lower entropy than its products of combustion, so the transition can only be in the one direction. An activity which can be run backwards is said to be *reversible*, and must take place at constant entropy. All real processes are *irreversible* to a greater or lesser extent, and the increase in entropy they entail is a measure of their irreversibility. It is also a consequence of the Second Law that no process can be more efficient than a reversible process. The increase in

entropy, therefore, is a measure of how efficient a process is compared to the
maximum possible.

Entropy is generally defined not as an absolute value, but in terms of the
change associated with the transfer of a small amount of heat:

$$\delta S = \frac{\delta H}{T}$$

where δS is the small change in entropy associated with the transfer of the
small amount of heat δH at absolute temperature T. This differential
equation must be evaluated by the mathematical process of integration (or
graphical or numerical equivalents of it) to find the change in entropy
occurring over a large change in other properties.

For water-steam, entropy is arbitrarily given the value of zero at 0°C (273 K).
Tables of values of entropy as a function of temperature and pressure (or other
properties) can then be calculated and charts can be plotted.

The charts (known as T-S charts) have the form shown in figure 15.1. Three
zones can be specified: Liquid, Mixture and Vapour. These are separated
from each other by the Liquid Line and the Saturated Vapour line. The lines
meet at the Critical Point, where the distinction between liquid and vapour
disappears.

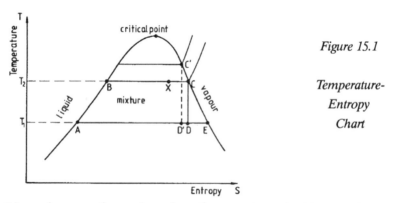

Figure 15.1

Temperature-
Entropy
Chart

Lines of evaporation and condensation are at constant temperature, and
those of reversible adiabatic operations are at constant entropy. Hence a
Carnot cycle (chapter 2) appears as a rectangle on the T-S chart.

Formation of steam at constant pressure

In the lower part of the liquid region, lines of constant pressure crowd so
closely together near the liquid line as to appear to coincide with it. With this
proviso in mind the formation of unit mass of steam can be illustrated on the
T-S chart.

Unit mass of feedwater at temperature T_1 is raised to a pressure corresponding to the desired evaporation temperature T_2 along a constant pressure line (which lies close to the liquid line) from A to B. At B, the temperature corresponds to the pressure. The next stage is the reception of latent heat from B to C at constant temperature, as the water evaporates. Once it has completely evaporated, further heating would move the state point up the inclined constant pressure superheat line. If the supply of latent heat is cut off during the evaporation phase, at point X, the result is wet steam of dryness fraction given by the ratio

$$\frac{BX}{BC}$$

Assuming a saturated steam cycle under ideal conditions, the expansion in the engine is a vertical line down from C to the initial temperature at D. The dryness fraction of the exhaust steam is

$$\frac{AD}{AE}$$

Had the initial steam pressure been higher, up to a point C', the final point D' would have a dryness fraction

$$\frac{AD'}{AE}$$

The conclusion is that the higher the boiler pressure, the wetter will be the exhaust steam. This fact has a profound effect on power plants. The existence of a wet exhaust does not need any theories of cylinder condensation: it is in the nature of steam.

Demonstrations on the T-S chart

Phenomena discussed in earlier chapters can be demonstrated on the T-S chart.

Horizontal lines such as AB (figure 15.2) represent isothermal evaporation, or in the opposite direction, condensation.

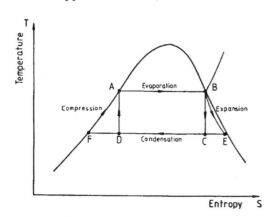

Figure 15.2

Processes on the Temperature-Entropy Chart

A vertical line such as *BC* represents ideal resisted expansion in which the maximum amount of work is done (Chapter 3). This shows that the steam must always become progressively wetter as the expansion proceeds. A line such as *BE* represents an unresisted expansion, or throttling process, in which no work is done. The steam becomes drier or possibly even superheated. A real engine expansion process would lie in between these two extremes (not illustrated on this chart).

A vertical line such as *DA* represents ideal compression condensing (Chapter 8).

The closed cycle *ABCDA* represents an ideal Carnot cycle between the liquid and vapour states. This is the cycle of theoretical perfection, but the need for the compression condensing step *DA* with its associated mechanical losses generally discourages its practical application.

The closed cycle *ABCDFA* is the Rankine cycle without superheat. This uses complete isothermal condensation and the only negative work required is that in the feed pump.

A property of the T-S chart is that the area enclosed by a state point moving in an ideal and frictionless cycle is the work done in that cycle. Readers are warned that this can be a dangerous concept; any friction at all invalidates it. Thus the area *ABCD* represents the maximum work which can be done between the temperature limits, while the area *ABECD*, which involves the friction (unresisted expansion) step *BE*, generates no work at all; it is all lost in the friction. Many inventors have worked with this concept of area, to their disappointment.

In the above, results which are already known have been illustrated on the chart. Given sufficient facility in its use, previously unknown phenomena may be investigated on the chart before the proposal is committed to hardware.

Theoretical cycles on a pressure-volume field

As an alternative to the T-S diagram, cycles may be plotted on a pressure-volume (P-V) field (figure 15.3).

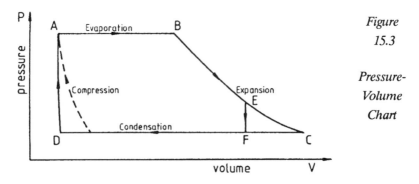

Figure 15.3

Pressure-Volume Chart

The Rankine cycle *ABCDA* has a long "toe" on the expansion line down to condenser pressure at *C*. This field can only be partially entered, and only with a turbine plant; large volumes at low pressures can be better dealt with by a steady flow process rather than an intermittent one.

The practical steam engine cycle cuts off the toe to give the cycle *ABEFDA*. This diagram has much the same shape as an indicator diagram, but must not be confused with it. It is an entirely different concept, being the pressure-volume history of a unit mass of water-steam as it goes all the way round the power plant; the indicator diagram is concerned solely with whatever steam happens to be within the cylinder at a given point in its motion.

The toe represents exhaust energy which is not converted to useful work. One way of using it, and thus approaching the Rankine ideal, was used on some triple-screw ships (e.g. the White Star liner *Olympic*). The outer propellers were driven by reciprocating engines, which exhausted into a turbine which drove the centre screw. This enabled the more flexible reciprocators to be used for manoeuvring, but recovered some of the lost work. Attempts such as this to recover some exhaust energy continued as long as the large reciprocating engine was significant. They had some measure of technical success, but complications in operation may have told against them economically.

The Carnot cycle would involve replacing the almost vertical feed pump line *DA* with a suitable adiabatic and frictionless step from some suitable point on the condensation line *CD* to *A*.

Glossary of Steam Terms

Adiabatic

Term used to describe a change in which heat is neither given nor rejected. 'Adiabatic and frictionless' is the ideal expansion process in an engine.

Air Condenser

A surface condenser which uses air as the cooling medium. May be used on automobiles or on railway locomotives to conserve water in arid lands.

Air Pump

Strictly, the pump used to extract air from a condenser. Since the condensate has a small volume relative to the air, it may extract the condensate as well.

Air Vessel

An iron bottle-shaped vessel attached neck downward by a T-junction at the delivery from a reciprocating pump. Compression of the air in the vessel acts as a shock absorber and reduces 'water hammer' or shock waves in the pipe.

Angle of Advance

The angle in excess of 90° by which an eccentric is in advance of the crank when an outside admission slide valve is used.

Atmospheric or Newcomen Engine

A primitive form of engine in which the vacuum following the condensation of steam on one side of the piston enables atmospheric pressure to exert a resultant force on the other.

Auxiliary Machinery

In marine usage, the many machines used to support the main engine – pumps for feed, extraction, condenser cooling, etc.

Axle

The shaft which carries the wheels of a vehicle.

Back Pressure

The pressure which resists the free exhaust of a steam engine or turbine.

Balance (or Bob) Weights

Weights attached to the crankshaft which help to neutralise forces arising from the crank and the big end of the connecting rod.

Barring Engine

A small auxiliary engine used to rotate a much larger one slowly for adjustment or repair.

Bash Valve

A valve operated by the piston itself as it nears the end of its stroke.

Beam Engine

The primitive form of steam engine originally used for mine drainage. A vertical cylinder acted on one end of a rocking beam, while the pump rods were suspended from the other. During the first half of the 19th century, when adapted for rotary motion, it was almost the standard type.

Big End

The end of the connecting rod which carries the crank pin bearing.

Blast Pipe

A steam exhaust pipe, arranged as a jet pump, used to augment the draught through a boiler fire.

Blow Down

The process of discharging a boiler under pressure by a low level cock; used to clear sediment.

Boiler

The pressure vessel in which water is converted into steam.

Bourdon Gauge

The ordinary pressure gauge which depends on the tendency of an elliptic tube to straighten out when subject to internal pressure. It is an inferential gauge which must be calibrated.

Brake Horse Power

Power as measured by a brake on the engine shaft. Better called Shaft Horse Power since there are other means than a brake of making this measurement.

Butterfly Valve

A circular disc, pivoted along its diameter, which can be used to close off a pipe. Its rapid action is sometimes advantageous, as when a marine engine needs to be controlled in a pitching ship. In water it needs to be used with care if water hammer is to be avoided.

Clack Valve

A valve in a pipe which closes automatically when the flow tends to reverse. A non-return valve.

Cock

A rapid action form of valve. Generally a rotating plug which is drilled along a diameter. The pipe is closed when the plug rotates through 90°. Special forms are Stop Cock for semi-permanent interruption of flow and Drain Cock for the removal of condensed water from a steam space. A two-way cock allows the flow to be diverted in either of two directions.

Compound Expansion

The dividing up of the expansion into a number of stages. In practice, normally refers to two-stage expansion.

Compression

The process which follows the closing of the exhaust valve at the end of the stroke. It may be referred to as cushioning.

Condenser

The device which turns exhaust steam back to water, either to conserve water or to lower the back pressure.

Connecting Rod

The rod which connects the reciprocating to the rotating part of an engine, i.e. the crosshead to the crank.

Convection

Flow due to differences of temperature and pressure in a fluid. Important in heat transfer between a fluid and a solid surface. (This is free convection; forced convection is the equivalent heat transfer process driven by a pump or fan.)

Corliss Valve

A rapid-acting semi-rotary slide valve much used on large low-speed mill engines.

Cornish Boiler

A single-flue shell boiler in a brickwork setting.

Cornish Engine

A beam pumping engine which utilised a fairly high degree of expansion. Particularly developed for mine drainage in Cornwall, later used for water supply pumping.

Critical Point (also critical pressure, temperature)

A point on the pressure-volume representation of fluid properties. Above the critical temperature, no pressure however great can liquify the fluid. May be important when fluids other than water-steam are used in an engine.

Crosshead

The structure at the junction of the connecting rod and the piston rod.

Damper

A device for controlling the air supply to a boiler fire.

Dead Centre

The engine position at either extremity of the stroke when neither thrust nor tension in the connecting rod can assist rotation. Inner dead centre (IDC) and outer dead centre (ODC) are relative to the cylinder. Top and bottom dead centre (TDC, BDC) are equivalent when the cylinder is above the crank.

Displacement Lubricator

A container of oil connected to the steam pipe near to the engine. As steam enters and condenses, oil is displaced into the engine for the lubrication of the valve and piston.

Double-Acting Engine

An engine in which the steam acts alternately on each side of the piston.

Double Beat Valve

A valve so designed that pressure forces are almost in equilibrium; hence it is easy to operate.

Draught

The pressure forcing air through the fire. Often measured in inches of water.

Drop Valve

See *Poppet Valve*

Dryness Fraction

The proportion of dry steam, as a fraction of the total steam/water mixture.

Duplex Pump

Two direct-acting pumps (i.e. pumps with the steam and water pump pistons on the same piston rod) side by side. The are made to work alternately by using each to operate the slide valve of the other.

Eccentric

A disc set off-centre on a shaft, generally used to drive a valve or pump.

Economizer

Boiler feed water heating pipes set in the path of the flue gases after they have left the boiler.

Edwards Air Pump

An effective reciprocating air pump which makes use of inertia forces to dispense with foot and bucket valves.

Efficiency

The proportion of the energy leaving a machine in the desired form to the total energy put into it. Not to be confused with effectiveness or reliability.

Ejector

A jet pump used for suction, typically to improve the vacuum in a condenser or as a bilge pump.

Emulsion

An intimate mixture of oil and water; may be used for lubrication in marine engines.

Enthalpy

A term for the energy transferred by a flowing fluid, particularly steam. Incorporates (and replaces) terms such as sensible heat, latent heat, heat of formation, etc.

Entropy

A mathematical concept of great use in the theory of thermodynamic processes. It has no straightforward physical interpretation, but has been associated with disorder or lack of structure.

Evaporative Condenser

An air-cooled surface over which there is a trickle of cold water. This evaporates and increases the effectiveness of the condenser.

Expansion

The practice of allowing steam trapped behind the piston to do further work as the pressure falls after inlet cut-off.

Expansion Ratio

The ratio of the maximum to the minimum volume of the cylinder.

Extraction Pump

The pump which removes condensate and perhaps air from the condenser. Also known as air pump when, as is most common, one pump is used for both duties.

Feed Heater

A device for warming the feed water before its entry into the boiler-economizer.

Feed Pump

The pump which supplies the boiler with water.

Field Tube

A form of boiler tube with a closed lower end and an axial supply of cold water.

Fink Gear

A simple form of reversing gear, rarely used nowadays.

Fire Bars

Bars which support the solid fuel in a boiler furnace.

Fireless Locomotive

A locomotive filled with hot (superheated) water from a stationary boiler. Used in areas where a fire hazard exists.

Fire Tubes

Tubes carrying the hot products of combustion which pass through the water space of a boiler.

Flash Boiler

A single tube kept at high temperature. Water introduced at one end is 'flashed' into steam for immediate use.

Flues

Ducts containing hot products of combustion which may or may not pass through or near to a boiler shell.

Flywheel

A heavy wheel mounted on the crank shaft to help ensure uniformity of rotation.

Forced Draught

The use of a mechanical means to force air through a boiler fire in order to intensify combustion.

Friction Back Pressure

The friction of an engine expressed in terms of a back pressure resisting the passage of the exhaust steam.

Friction Horsepower

The power needed to overcome the friction of an engine.

Funnel

The chimney of a marine or locomotive installation.

Fusible Plug

A plug of low melting point alloy set into a furnace crown. In the event of overheating, the plug melts and water escapes onto the fire.

Gauge, Pressure

A device to indicate the pressure in the boiler, or elsewhere. See also *Bourdon Gauge*.

Gauge, Water

A glass tube connected to the boiler at each end so as to indicate the level of water.

Gland

A component of the stuffing box which seals a rotating or sliding shaft which passes through a pressure vessel wall.

Governor

A device (usually centrifugal) used to limit changes of engine speed when the load is changed.

Gudgeon Pin

The bearing pin at the connecting-rod/piston-rod junction in the crosshead.

Hackworth Valve Gear

A reversing and regulating gear based on one eccentric and on a sliding block of variable inclination, formerly popular for marine uses. The parent of many other types of valve gear.

Heat Engine

Any engine which converts heat to work. Includes steam and internal combustion engines, but not turbines or electric motors.

Heating Surface

The area subject, directly or otherwise, to heat from the boiler fire.

Horsepower

A unit of power introduced by James Watt, being superseded by the kilowatt. 1 HP is equivalent to 0.746 kW.

Hotwell

The tank which receives feed water on a condensing engine.

Hunting

A fairly long period speed variation induced by a governor tending to overcorrect for changes in engine speed.

Indicator

An instrument which draws a graph of steam pressure on a base of piston stroke. The older mechanical type were much used in engine investigation and originated the term 'indicated horsepower'. The modern electronic type are still used in internal combustion engine research.

Induced Draught

The use of steam jets, fans or chimneys to draw air through the boiler fire.

Initial Condensation

An early theory, now superseded, to account for the presence of water during the expansion in a steam cylinder.

Injector

A form of steam jet pump used as a boiler feed pump.

Inside Admission

Steam supplied between the two spools of a piston valve, with exhaust at the ends.

Isentropic

An ideal process in an engine cycle; the same as 'adiabatic and frictionless'.

Jacket, Steam

The jacketing of a cylinder by high pressure steam, in an effort to improve efficiency. Shown not to work both in theory and practice, and now obsolete.

Jet Pump

A pump working by entraining a fluid in a jet of steam. See injector, ejector.

Joy Valve Gear

A radial valve gear which, picking its motion from a point on a linkwork connected to the connecting rod, needs no eccentric. Thence similar to the Hackworth.

Kinetic Theory

A theory which accounts for many fluid properties in terms of molecular motion.

Kitson Valve Gear

A radial valve gear, similar in principle to the Walshaert, which picks up a rotary motion from a point on the coupling rod; formerly used on steam trams.

Lancashire Boiler

A shell boiler with two furnace flues, formerly very common for land purposes.

Lap, Steam and Exhaust

The amount by which a slide valve overlaps the ports when in mid-position.

Latent Heat

The energy absorbed by unit mass of fluid as it changes from the liquid to the vapour state.

Lead to Steam

The amount by which the steam port is open when the piston stroke is about to begin.

Linking Up

The process of reducing power, generally at high speed, by operation of a link motion.

Link Motion

A controlling and reversing device utilising two eccentrics. There are three principal types: Stephenson, Gooch and Allan. The Stephenson is now the best known.

Locomotive Engine

A self-propelled steam power unit.

Manhole

An access opening in a boiler or similar vessel.

Marshall Valve Gear

A radial gear very similar in its action to the Hackworth.

Mitre Valve

See *Poppet Valve*

Monotube Boiler

A boiler formed from a single tube. Feed water enters at one end and steam leaves at the other.

Motion

A general term for the various moving links, rods and bars used in a steam engine.

Mud Plug

A plug which can be used to remove sediment from the lower parts of a steam boiler.

Natural Draught

The use of a tall chimney or funnel to draw air through a boiler fire. The typical mill chimney needed a height of about 45 m (150 ft) to produce a draught of 25 mm (1 inch) water gauge.

Newcomen Engine

See *Atmospheric Engine*

Nozzle

A device to produce a jet of fluid which has an ordered uni-directional flow.

'Ordinary' Steam Engine

A simple double-acting engine with exposed cranks and connecting rod and utilising a flat slide valve.

Outside Admission

> The normal way of operating a piston or slide valve, with the steam supply to the outside of the valve and the exhaust from the inside.

Outside Lap

> The amount by which a slide valve overlaps the steam ports when it is in mid position.

Overhung Crank

> A crank on the end of a shaft, with bearings on the inside only. Widely used on locomotive engines.

Partial Pressure

> The contribution of one component of a mixture of gases to the pressure of the whole, for example a mixture of air and steam. For some purposes, such a mixture can be treated as the sum of its various components, each exerting its own partial pressure.

Pipes

> The many different pipes can be distinguished by terms such as feed, steam, exhaust, fuel, etc.

Piston Rod

> The circular rod which connects the piston to the crosshead.

Piston Valve

> A circular form of slide valve in which the lateral forces are balanced.

Plug

> A semi-permanent means of closing a hole in a pressure vessel. Special cases: fusible plug, drain plug, mud plug.

Poppet (or Mitre or Drop) Valve

> An axi-symmetric valve generally worked by a cam, similar to those in an internal combustion engine. Used in high superheat engines.

Port

> The opening in a valve face which communicates with the working cylinder.

Priming

> (In boilers) The sudden release of steam throughout the boiler leading to a very wet steam-water mix (often in the form of a spray or foam) at exit. Can happen due to impurities in feed water or to a sudden fall in pressure.

Quadruple Expansion

An engine in which the expansion is carried out in four successive stages. Used at sea for large ships with steam pressure in excess of 14 bar (200 psi).

Radial Motion

A regulating, controlling and reversing valve gear of the more precise type. In particular, if the motion is moved from the ahead to the astern position while the piston is (at rest) at top dead centre, the valve does not move.

Radiation

Linear transmission of (heat) energy, as from a fire.

Ratio of Expansion

The ratio of the volume of steam in a cylinder at release to the volume at cut-off.

Receiver

The vessels into which steam discharges between one stage of expansion and the next. Often simply the pipe connecting the cylinders.

Relief Valve

A valve designed to control pressure by releasing excess steam. Often confused with *Safety Valve*.

Return Crank

A light crank arm mounted outside an overhung crank, used for driving valve gear on outside cylinder locomotives.

Reversing Engine

A small auxiliary engine which works the reversing gear of a much larger one.

Rod

See *Connecting Rod, Piston Rod, Tail Rod*.

Safety Valve

A essential valve which will release steam if the pressure rises above the safe working pressure. Strictly for emergency use, but often confused both in speech and practice with a *relief valve*.

Saturated Steam

Pure steam with water droplets, at the pressure which corresponds to its temperature.

Second Law of Thermodynamics

One of the most fundamental of all natural laws. Among its consequences are the precluding of any form of perpetual motion and the setting of an upper limit to the efficiency of any *heat engine*.

Sensible Heat

Heat applied to water which changes its temperature. Now generally treated in terms of *enthalpy*.

Shell Boiler

Any boiler which mainly consists of one large (usually cylindrical) pressure vessel.

Shuttle Valve

A slide valve operated by steam, used when rapid action is required at the end of a piston stroke. Used particularly for direct acting boiler feed pumps.

Simple Engine

An engine in which the steam expands only once (in contrast to a compound or triple expansion engine).

Single-Acting Engine

An engine in which the steam only acts on one side of the piston.

Slide Valve

A valve which works by sliding over ports to cover and uncover them. The type used to control the flow into and out of the cylinder of an *ordinary steam engine*.

Stay Bolts

Bolts inside a boiler supporting flat surfaces subject to steam pressure.

Steam Chest

The boxlike chamber on an engine cylinder which encloses the ports and slide valve.

Stop Valve

The screw-down valve closest to the engine on the steam supply pipe.

Stuffing Box

The assembly which prevents leakage when a sliding or rotating shaft works through a pressure vessel wall. Generally applied to the piston rod and cylinder cover.

Tail Rod

An extension of the *piston rod* through the cylinder head. Used on very large pistons to reduce loading on the cylinder walls.

Tandem Engine

A compound engine whose two cylinders are in line on a common piston rod and work on the same crank.

Thermodynamics

The science of the relationships between work and heat.

Throttle Valve

A control valve which is partially closed to reduce the pressure of the steam. Since no work is done in the throttle, the emerging steam may be dried or even slightly superheated.

Total Heat

The term formerly used for the heat required to produce unit mass of steam from water at freezing point. Now superseded by the more general term *enthalpy*.

Traction Engine

A locomotive engine working on the road rather than rails.

Triple Expansion Engine

An engine in which the expansion is carried out in three successive stages. At one time the most common type of all for sea-going ships.

Uniflow Engine

An engine in which steam is admitted at the cylinder head and exhausted through a belt of ports exposed in the cylinder wall when the piston nears the end of its stroke. The most efficient of all piston engines for constant speed duties.

Vacuum

Strictly, a region of space in which there is no matter. Used rather loosely to refer to any pressure below that of the atmosphere.

Walshaert's Valve Gear

A radial valve gear of Belgian origin which became very widely used for railway locomotives.

Water Tube Boiler

A boiler in which the heating surface consists largely of relatively small diameter tubes.

Watt Parallel Motion

A linkwork used to guide a rod along a very nearly straight path, instead of a crosshead guide.

Weigh Shaft

The shaft joining the reversing links on a multi-cylinder engine, which ensures that they all operate together.

Willans Line

The graphical representation of constant speed engine characteristics, found experimentally to be very close to a straight line.

Winding Engine

The engine used for lifting and lowering the cage in a mine shaft.

Wiredrawing

A gradual fall in pressure of steam in a cylinder arising from the slow rate of closure of a slide valve.

Bibliography

The steam engine has passed through the three phases of scientific and engineering research, day to day engineering practise, and obsolescence. The published literature falls into corresponding groups: proceedings of learned societies in the nineteenth century, university and college textbooks in the first half of the twentieth century, and historical and enthusiast publications in the second half.

The publications listed below are a representative selection of all of these. They are arranged roughly in the same order as the chapters of the text, but many of them will overlap both the text and each other. All of them will contain further references which are well worth following up. Some of the textbooks listed have been through several editions, and other similar ones exist.

Most of the material will be available in the libraries of universities with established engineering faculties, and all of it could be obtained by such a library through the inter-library loan system. Large public libraries should also be able to supply it. Many of the textbooks listed (and others similar) might be found in the second-hand book market; the enthusiast and historical publications are mostly currently in print.

Periodicals

Three periodicals may be specifically mentioned as of direct interest:

Funnel is the journal of the Steam Boat Association of Great Britain (SBA). Details of the Association and availability of back numbers are obtainable from the publisher.

SIMEC Magazine is published by the Stuart International Model Engineering Club (SIMEC), 54 Berkshire Road, Henley-on-Thames, Oxfordshire, RG9 1NA, England.

The periodical *Steam Power* (formerly *Light Steam Power*) is published from 106A Derby Road, Loughborough, LE11 0AG, England.

Since every issue of these journals contains material of interest, specific articles from them are not listed below.

Books and Articles

Thomas Newcomen: the prehistory of the steam engine
L.T.C. Rolt, David & Charles 1963

A Short History of the Steam Engine

    H.W. Dickinson, Babcock & Wilcox/Cambridge Univ. Press 1938

James Watt and the Steam Engine

    H.W. Dickinson and Rhys Jenkins, Moorland (2nd ed) 1981 (ISBN 0 903485 92 3)

The Steam Engine in Industry

    George Watkins, Moorland 1979 (ISBN 0 903485 67 2)

The Industrial Archaeology of the Stationary Steam Engine

    R.A. Buchanan and G. Watkins, Allen Lane, London 1976 (ISBN 0 7139 0604 9)

A History of the Institution of Mechanical Engineers 1847-1947

    R.H. Parsons, I. Mech. E., London 1947

The Mechanicals: progress of a profession

    L.T.C. Rolt, Heinemann, London 1967

Thermodynamics for Engineers

    J.A. Ewing, Cambridge Univ. Press, several editions 1920-1936

Thermodynamic Tables and other data (Steam Tables in ft lb F units)

    R.W. Haywood, Cambridge Univ. Press 1960

Thermodynamic and Transport properties of Fluids (Steam Tables in SI units)

    Y.R. Mayhew & G.F.C. Rogers, Blackwell, Oxford 1980 (ISBN 0 631 12891 3)

The Automatic Control of Small Boilers

    J.A. Crabtree, Trans. Newcomen Soc. **43** 93-111 (1970-71)

Boiler Explosions and their records

    E.R. Marten, Proc. I.Mech.E 130 (1866) and 179 (1870)

The Efficient Use of Steam

    O. Lyle, H.M.S.O. 1947

The Steam Engine and other Heat Engines

    J.A. Ewing, Cambridge Univ. Press, 4th ed (1926)

The Steam Engine

    J. Bourne, Longman Green Longman & Roberts, London 1861

Steam Steering Engines in the "Great Eastern" Steamship
J.M. Gray, Proc. I. Mech. E. 267 (1867)

The Steam Engine
D.K. Clark, Blackie, London 1891

The Steam Engine and Gas and Oil Engines
John Perry, Macmillan, London 1899

The Uniflow Steam Engine
F.B.Perry, Proc. I. Mech. E. 731-764 (1920)

Some notes on the History of the Uniflow Engine
A. Throp, Trans. Newcomen Soc. **43** 19-39 (1970-71)

The Compound Locomotive
J.T. van Riemsdijk, Trans. Newcomen Soc. **43** (1970-71), **44** (1971-72) and **45** (1972-73)

New Reversing and Expansive Valve Gear
D. Joy, Proc. I. Mech. E. 418 (1880)

Balancing of Reciprocating Engines
W.E. Dalby, Proc. I. Mech. E. 197-217 (1908)

The Steam Launch
R.M. Mitchell, Patrick Stevens, Cambridge 1982 (ISBN 0 85059 609 2)

Steamboats and Steamships of the British Isles
SBA 1988 (ISBN 0 9513158 0 3)

Steamboats and Modern Steam Launches
Bill Durham (ed), Howell-North Books, San Diego, California 1981

Non-Condensing Steam-Engine Trials
P.W. Willans, Proc I.C.E. (1888)

Steam-Engine Trials
P.W. Willans, Proc I.C.E. **CXIV** 2 (1893)

Experimental Marine Engine and the Alternative-centre Testing Machine in the Walker Engineering Laboratories of University College, Liverpool
H.S. Hele-Shaw, Proc. I. Mech. E. 386 (1891)

Locomotive Testing Stations
D.R. Carling, Trans. Newcomen Soc. **45** 105-182 (1972-73)

INDEX

References to terms defined in the Glossary (pages 103-113) are shown in boldface. This index was prepared using MACREX indexing software.

thrutcher 62
torque
  measurement 90-91
    differential gear 91
    strain gauge 91
total heat **116**
traction engine **116**
triple expansion engine **116**
T-S chart 98
tube, Field 27
turbine 31, 59, 101
turbulence 22-23, 32
  stimulators 23
Twain, Mark 25

U
uniflow engine 65-67, **116**
universities 44
Unwin, William C 44

V
vacuum 6, **116**
valve
  bash 67
  cam operated 66
  drop 66
  events 64
  exhaust, auxiliary 67
  piston 54
  poppet 56, 67
  slide 53-54, 64
valve diagram 74-76
  Reuleaux 74-76

valve gear 69-75
  link 71
  radial 72
  Allen 71
  Bremme 73
  Gooch 71
  Hackworth 73
  Joy 73
  Kitson 74
  Marshall 73
  Stephenson 71
  Walshaert 74
Vasa 84
volume, clearance 40-41, 62, 66

W
Walshaert's valve gear 74, **116**
water-steam substance 13
water tube boiler 26, **117**
Watt, James 1, 39, 44, 77, 89
Watt parallel motion **117**
weigh shaft **117**
wetness fraction 17
wet steam 17, 37
Willans, Kyrle W 39
Willans' line 93-95, **117**
Willans, Peter W 57, 93
winding engine **117**
windmill, characteristics 92
wiredrawing **117**
work 8
  negative 9